TO THE ENDS OF THE EARTH

AN IN-DEPTH STUDY OF THE BOOK OF ACTS

The Birth and Early Expansion of the Church

by Jay G. Borkert

Purposeful Design Publications is the publishing division of the Association of Christian Schools International (ACSI) and is committed to the ministry of Christian school education, to enable Christian educators and schools worldwide to effectively prepare students for life. As the publisher of textbooks, trade books, and other educational resources within ACSI, Purposeful Design Publications strives to produce biblically sound materials that reflect Christian scholarship and stewardship and that address the identified needs of Christian schools around the world.

Unless otherwise identified, all Scripture quotations are taken from the Holy Bible, New King James Version (NKJV), © 1982 by Thomas Nelson, Inc. Used by permission. All rights reserved.

Printed in the United States of America
26 25 24 23 22 21 20   10 11 12 13 14 15 16

Borkert, Jay G.
    To the ends of the earth: An in-depth study of the book of Acts
    ISBN 978-1-58331-132-5 Student edition Catalog #MBTES

Editorial team: John Conaway, Gina Brandon
Design: Michael Riester
Illustration: Aline Heiser
Cover Image: Don Farrell, photodisc.com

Purposeful Design Publications
A Division of ACSI
731 Chapel Hills • Colorado Springs, CO 80920
Member Care: 800.367.0798 • www.purposefuldesign.com

Contents

i

| Date: Present Day | Place: Classroom | Roman Emperor: Extinct | Local Ruler: Teacher |

4

You are about to embark on a
fascinating New Testament journey
that will carry you to hostile cities, lofty
temples, and raging seas. You will meet a
wealthy soldier, a stinky tanner, a reluctant
king, a godly businesswoman, a sleepy
student, a faithful martyr, and many other
interesting characters. You will stand in
crowds of eager listeners, flee from the
stones of angry mobs, debate with religious
Pharisees, talk with intellectual philosophers,
and pray with coarse sailors.

You will be witnessing the birth and
expansion of the early Christian church.
Along the journey, your mind will be
stretched and your values will be challenged.
You will learn much about the truth of
Scripture and how, by applying it, you can
impact your world. Read carefully, study
diligently, and you will be enriched.

May your life be changed for His glory by
the acts of the apostles—the book of Acts.

Jay G. Borkert

1 **Who wrote the book of Acts?** SOLVE THE MYSTERY

Complete the following sentences to find out:

a. The author of the book of Luke is _____.

b. Luke wrote this book to someone named _____. (Read Luke 1:1–4.)

c. Luke set out to write an "orderly account" about the life of _____.

d. The author of Acts also wrote another account to _____. (See Acts 1:1.)

e. The author of Acts refers to his "former account" of Jesus' life, the book of _____.

f. Therefore, the author of Acts must be _____.

Did you know? Luke was a doctor (see Colossians 4:14) and also a Gentile.

2 **When was Acts written?**

Many different dates have been given for the writing of Acts. It is likely that it was written after Paul's first imprisonment and before Jerusalem fell to the Romans in A.D. 70, since the author makes no mention of that event. Acts was probably written between A.D. _____ and _____.

3 **What is the theme of Acts?**

Below is a puzzle called a quote fall. The letters for the theme of the book of Acts are scrambled and arranged in columns above the boxes. Fill in the blank boxes using the scrambled letters in the columns above them to find the correct letters.

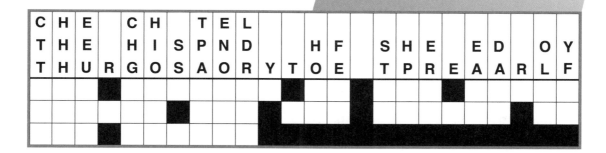

4 **The theme verse of Acts is Acts 1:8.** Write it below. Then memorize it.

5 **What is the approximate** time span **of Acts?** (2 x 300 ÷ 4 + 90) ÷ 8 = [   ] years.

6 This study, TO THE ENDS OF THE EARTH, divides the book of Acts into eight parts, or units. **Use the contents page to find the unit titles, and add a word to complete each title below:**

Unit 1 A _____ Beginning
    1. After the Resurrection
    2. The Holy Spirit Comes
    3. Peter Heals a Beggar

Unit 2 From Zeal to _____
    4. Characteristics of the Early Church
    5. Punishment and Persecution
    6. The Choosing of the Seven
    7. The Death of Stephen

Unit 3 From _____ to the Ends of the Earth
    8. The Church Persecuted, Scattered, and Growing
    9. Saul Converted, Aeneas Healed, Dorcas Restored to Life
    10. Peter's Vision and Cornelius' Conversion
    11. The Church Accepts Gentiles
    12. Peter's Escape and Herod's Death

Unit 4 Missionary _____ One and Jerusalem Council
    13. Paul and Barnabas Travel to Pisidian Antioch
    14. Iconium to Derbe and Back to Antioch
    15. Jerusalem Council Meets, Paul and Barnabas Part

Unit 5 _____ Journey Two
    16. Paul and Silas at Phillipi
    17. Paul at Thessalonica, Berea, and Athens
    18. Paul at Corinth and Ephesus

Unit 6 Missionary Journey _____
    19. Paul's Ministry at Ephesus
    20. Preaching in Troas, Farewell in Miletus

Unit 7 Trials in Jerusalem and _____
    21. Farewell in Tyre, Arrest in Jerusalem
    22. Paul Declares His Roman Citizenship
    23. Paul Speaks to the Council and Foils a Plot
    24. Paul's Trial before Felix
    25. Paul's Trial before Festus and Appeal to Caesar
    26. Paul's Witness to King Agrippa II

Unit 8 Paul's Journey to _____
    27. Paul's Shipwreck
    28. Paul's Ministry on Malta, House Arrest in Rome

Use this page to help you pronounce the names of the cities, regions, and islands that you will read about in Acts. Pronunciations given are from *Unger's Bible Dictionary* (Moody Press 1966) and are the most commonly used. The pronunciation symbols are from *Merriam-Webster Online Dictionary*.

Pronunciation Symbols

& as *a* and *u* in abrupt

& as *e* in kitten

&r as *ur/er* in further

a as *a* in ash

A as *a* in ace

ä as *o* in mop

au as *ou* in out

ch as *ch* in chin

e as *e* in bet

E as *ea* in easy

g as *g* in go

i as *i* in hit

I as *i* in ice

j as *j* in job

[ng] as *ng* in sing

O as *o* in go

o as *aw* in law

oi as *oy* in boy

th as *th* in thin

[th] as *th* in the

ü as *oo* in loot

u as *oo* in foot

y as *y* in yet

zh as *si* in vision

Pronunciations

CITIES

Alexandria / "a-lig-'zan-drE-&

Amphipolis / am-'fi-p&-l&s

Antioch / 'an-tE-"äk

Apollonia / "a-p&-'lO-nE-&

Assos / 'a-säs

Athens / 'a-th&nz

Attalia / &-'ta-lE-&

Berea / b&-'rE-&

Caesarea / "sE-z&-'rE-&

Cenchrea / 'sen-krE-&

Cindus / 'sin-d&s

Corinth / 'kor-&n(t)th

Damascus / d&-'mas-k&s

Derbe / 'd&r-(")bE

Ephesus / 'e-f&-s&s

Forum of Appius / 'a-pE-&s

Iconium / I-'kO-nE-&m

Jerusalem / j&-'rü-s(&-)l&m

Lasea / 'lA-sE-&

Lystra / 'lis-tr&

Miletus / mI-'lE-t&S

Myra / 'mI-r&

Neapolis / nE-'a-p&-lis

Paphos / 'pA-"fäs

Patara / p&-'tä-r&

Perga / 'p&r-g&

Philippi / 'fi-l&-"pI

Phoenix / 'fE-niks

Pisidian / p&-'si-dE-&n

Ptolemais / "tä-l&-'mA-&s

Puteoli / pyu-'tE-&-"lI

Rhegium / 'rE-jE-&m

Rome / 'rOm

Salamis / 'sa-l&-m&s

Salmone / 'sal-"mO-n&

Seleucia / s&-'lü-sh(E-)&

Syracuse / 'sir-&-"kyüs

Tarsus / 'tär-s&s

Thessalonica / "the-s&-'lä-ni-k&

Troas / 'trO-"as

Trogyllium / trO-'jil-y&m

REGIONS

Achaia / &-'kE-y&

Asia / 'A-zh&, -sh&

Bithynia / b&-'thi-nE-&

Chios / 'kI-"äs

Cilicia / s&-'li-sh(E-)&

Cos / 'käs

Crete / 'krEt, var. 'krE-tE

Cyprus / 'sI-pr&s

Galatia / g&-'lA-sh(E-)&

Greece / 'grEs

Italy / 'i-t&l-E

Lycia / 'li-sh(E-)&

Macedonia / "ma-s&-'dO-nE-&

Malta / 'mol-t&

Mysia / 'mi-sh(E-)&

Palestine / 'pa-l&-"stIn

Pamphylia / pam-'fi-lE-&

Phoenicia / fi-'ni-sh(E-)&

Phrygia / 'fri-j(E-)&

Pisidia / p&-'si-dE-&

Rhodes / 'rOdz

Samos / 'sA-"mäs

Samothrace / 'sa-m&-"thrAs

Syria / 'sir-E-&

Thyatira / "thI-&-'tI-r&

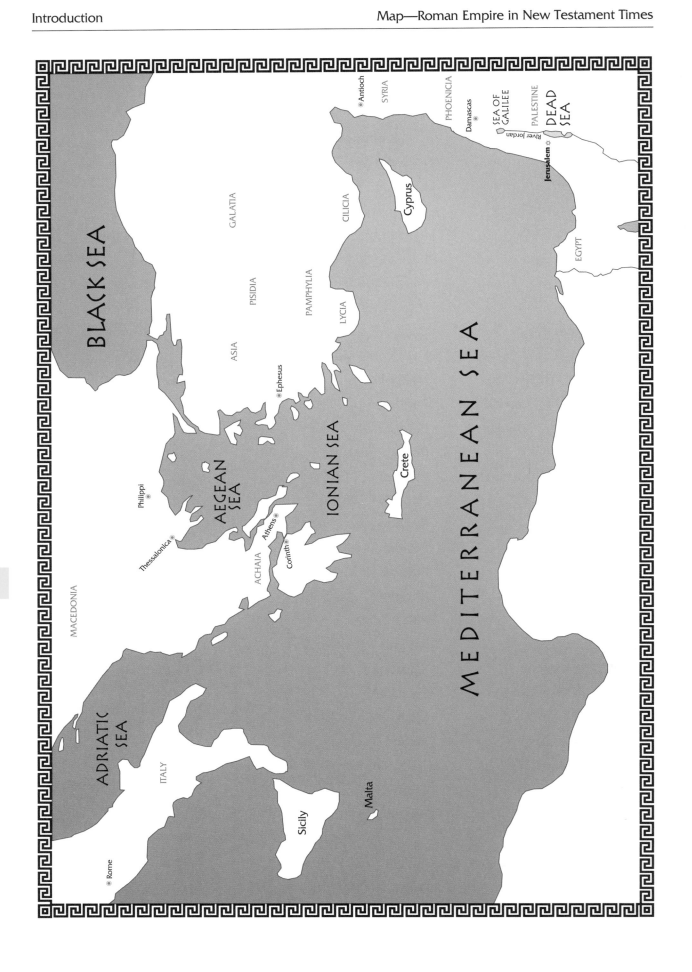

8

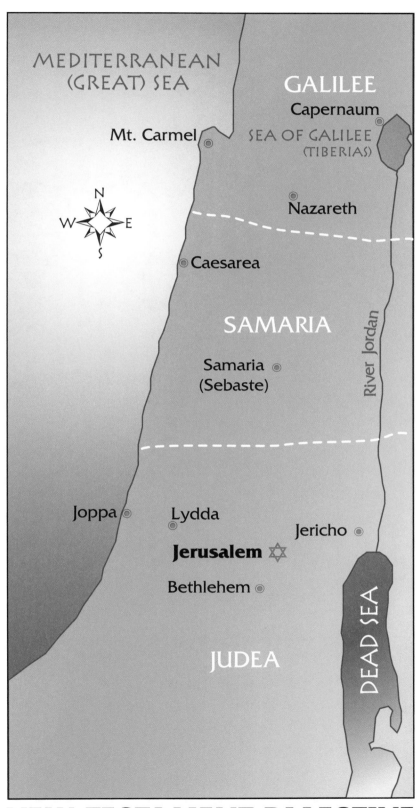

NEW TESTAMENT PALESTINE

· THE ROAD TO EMMAUS ·

A POWERFUL BEGINNING

11

| Date: A.D. 30 | Place: Jerusalem | Roman Emperor: Tiberius | Local Ruler: Herod Antipas |

1 Verse 2 of the first chapter of Acts speaks of clear commandments, or instructions, that Jesus gave the apostles before He ascended. **What were they?** (Read Matthew 28:19–20)

a.

b.

c.

2 Complete **the crossword puzzle.** Use the clues below, and Acts 1:1–12 for help.

Across

1 The apostles received ___ from the Holy Spirit.
5 Jesus' post-resurrection ministry lasted ___ days.
6 Jesus showed He was alive by many ___ proofs.
7 John had baptized his followers with ___.
8 The gospel would be taken to every part of the ___.

Down

2 Jesus said the apostles would be His ___.
3 Jesus spoke about the ___ of God.
4 The apostles saw Jesus ascend into ___.
7 Jesus told His apostles to ___ in Jerusalem.

3 Some people envision the resurrected Jesus as a ghost, but they have an incorrect idea about the risen Savior. Read Luke 24:36–39 and 42–43, which prove that Jesus was not a ghost during His post-resurrection ministry. **What two things could Jesus do that ghosts cannot do?**

1. _____

2. _____

4 According to verse 7, **when will the kingdom of God come?**

_____

5 **What three promises did Jesus make to His disciples?**

1.

2.

3.

12

⑥ **Fill in the blanks to reveal the Gs of the Holy Spirit:**

G __ __ __ of God dwelling in us

g __ __ __ __ us power.

⑨ **List the eleven apostles.**

1. _____   7. _____
2. _____   8. _____
3. _____   9. _____
4. _____   10. _____
5. _____   11. _____
6. _____

> " *Judas is a reminder that we can be very near to the kingdom but not enter into it.*
>
> —Mike McGorman "

ANALOGY

⑦ Acts 1:8 speaks of being a witness in different places. **Think of your town or city as Jerusalem. What would each of the following represent?**

a. **Judea** _____

b. **Samaria** _____

c. **the end of the earth** _____

⑩ We see in verse 14 that Jesus' brothers were among those who met in the upper room. **Read Mark 6:3 and list Jesus' half brothers.**

a. _____
b. _____
c. _____
d. _____

13

⑧ **What significance does verse 11 have in your life?**

11 **The first chapter of Acts tells us the following about Judas, the betrayer:**

a.

b.

c.

12 Verse 25 says that Judas went "to his own place." **Where do you think that was?**
_____

13 The apostles knew that someone should be chosen to take Judas' place. **Complete the following sentences, telling three things they did in order to pick another disciple:**

1. They chose two men who had been with them

2. They prayed that God would

3. They cast lots, and the lot fell to

_____

Key Verse

But you shall receive power when the Holy Spirit has come upon you; and you shall be witnesses to Me in Jerusalem, and in all Judea and Samaria, and to the end of the earth.

Acts 1:8

MEDITATION Think prayerfully about the content of Acts 1, noting the qualities of the early Christians. **In the back of your workbook, write a paragraph about what God has revealed to you in this chapter.**

14 **Find and read the verses below from chapter 1 of Acts. Complete the sentences, telling some things these first-century Christians did.**

vv. 4–8: They _____ to what Jesus said.

v. 10: They looked toward heaven as

_____ .

v. 11: They heard _____ predict that Jesus would return.

v. 13: They stayed in _____ .

v. 14: The disciples, Jesus' brothers, and _____ prayed continually.

vv. 21–26: They chose _____ to replace Judas as a twelfth disciple.

What's It Mean?

apostle—Sent one. The twelve apostles, and later Matthias, were chosen by God (v. 2) and were given the same authority as the prophets of the Old Testament. Apparently, a requirement for an apostle was that he must have witnessed the ministry, death, and resurrection of Christ (v. 22).

ascension—Christ's going into heaven.

casting lots—A decision-making process similar to drawing straws. In this case those involved trusted that God caused the results (v. 26).

martyr—One who chooses to die rather than deny his religious beliefs.

post-resurrection—The time after Jesus' resurrection.

All Right! ☐ Yes ☐ No
I read chapter 1. ☐ Yes, but I have questions.

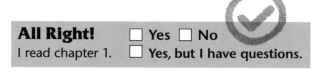

14

Date: Circa A.D. 30	Place: Jerusalem	Roman Emperor: Tiberius	Local Ruler: Herod Antipas

1 **Who do you think** "they" **were in verse 1?** _____

2 **Complete the phrases for the sounds and sights that accompanied the coming of the Holy Spirit.**
"And suddenly there came a _____ from heaven, as of a _____ mighty _____.…Then there appeared to them _____ _____, as of _____, and one sat upon each of them" (Acts 2:2–3).

3 **Why do you think the time and place were right for this great event?** (See v. 5.)

Note: *For Christians the significance of Pentecost is the descent of the Holy Spirit on the New Testament church, recorded later in this chapter.*

4 **Complete the phrase—***When the people heard the apostles speaking in their own language, they were* (see v. 7)

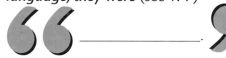
" _____ . "

5 **What** **condition** **did some of the crowd believe the apostles were in?**
(See vv. 13–15.) _____

6 Peter, in his message to the crowd, quoted from Joel 2:28–32, where Joel prophesies that God will pour out His Spirit on all people.

Is **this beginning to happen in Acts 2?**
☐ Yes ☐ No

Carefully read verses 17 and 18 and answer the questions below:
Was the Spirit to be poured out on
only the parents?   ☐ Yes ☐ No
only older **people?**   ☐ Yes ☐ No
only men?   ☐ Yes ☐ No
only the rich?   ☐ Yes ☐ No
Can anybody **receive the Holy Spirit?**
☐ Yes ☐ No

DIGGING   DEEPER

7 **To learn more about God's awesome character, read verse 2:23 carefully. Read carefully each verse below. Note the words in** *italics* **and check their meaning under** *What's It Mean.* **In the box on the following page, complete the truth that is found in all these verses.**

- Peter, an apostle of Jesus Christ, to the pilgrims of the *Dispersion* in Pontus, Galatia, Cappadocia, Asia, and Bithynia, *elect* according to the *foreknowledge* of God the Father, in sanctification of the Spirit, for obedience and sprinkling of the blood of Jesus Christ: Grace to you and peace be multiplied (1 Peter 1:1–2).

- He [Christ] indeed was *foreordained* before the foundation of the world, but was manifest in these last times for you (1 Peter 1:20).

- For whom He *foreknew*, He also *predestined* to be conformed to the image of His Son, that He might be the firstborn among many brethren (Romans 8:29).

15

- God has not cast away His people whom He *foreknew*. Or do you not know what the Scripture says of Elijah, how he pleads with God against Israel (Romans 11:2).

- But you are a *chosen* generation, a royal priesthood, a holy nation, His own special people, that you may proclaim the praises of Him who called you out of darkness into His marvelous light (1 Peter 2:9).

- For truly against Your holy Servant Jesus, whom You anointed, both Herod and Pontius Pilate, with the Gentiles and the people of Israel, were gathered together to do whatever Your hand and Your purpose *determined* before to be done (Acts 4:27–28).

- Now when the Gentiles heard this, they were glad and glorified the word of the Lord. And as many as had been *appointed* to eternal life believed (Acts 13:48).

- For we are His workmanship, created in Christ Jesus for good works, which God prepared beforehand that we should walk in them (Ephesians 2:10).

Because God is _____ ,
He _____ all things,
including our salvation.

8 Read **verses 22 and 23 together. Could the word** *you* **in verse 23 refer to us as well as the men of Israel?**
☐ **Yes** ☐ **No** Explain:

9 Complete **the following verses:**
"*. . . whom God _____ up, having loosed the pains of death, because it was not possible that He should be held by it.…[he] spoke concerning the _____ of the Christ, that His soul was not left in _____, nor did His flesh see _____. This Jesus God has raised up, of which we are all _____*" (Acts 2:24, 31–32).
What can you conclude from these verses?

10 Who **are the "we … all" of verse 32?**
_____

11 Read Acts 2:38 and Acts 10:42–48.
According to these verses, when does a person receive the Holy Spirit?

12 According to verse 39, **who will receive the promise of the Holy Spirit?**
_____

13 How many **believers were added to the early church that day?** (See v. 41.)
_____

14 **FELLOWSHIP OF BELIEVERS ANAGRAM**
Below are anagrams made with words used in describing the young church in Acts 2:42–47. Read **through this passage and** study **the clues below. Unscramble each word and** complete **it on the line provided.** Check **the box beside each characteristic you have** seen **or** experienced **in your own church.**
(Not every word comes directly from the Bible.)

u n d i n e c o t
☐ [Believers] **c**_____ steadfastly in the apostles' doctrine.

h o p w e l l i f s
☐ They had **f**_____ with one another.

o n i c o n m u m
☐ They broke bread in what we call **c**_____ today.

a y r p
☐ They continued to **p**_____.

g o t h t r e e
☐ All believers were **t**_____.

e d s e n
☐ They shared with those who had **n**_____.

e t a
☐ They broke bread and **a**_____ in their homes.

d a l g
☐ Their hearts were **g**_____.

a s p i d e r
☐ They **p**_____ God.

r o v f a
☐ They enjoyed **f**_____ among those in Jerusalem.

d a d d e
☐ As a result, God **a**_____ to their numbers daily.

15 Should **the church today be** the same **as the early church described in verses 42–47?** ☐ Yes ☐ No
Why or why not?

16 **How is** your church **like the New Testament church?** List **as many ways as you can:**

★
★
★
★
★

17 List **four** specific **ways the group of Christians you hang out with (at church, school, or in your neighborhood) can show the** characteristics **of the early church:**

1._____

2._____

3._____

4._____

And they continued steadfastly in the apostles' doctrine and fellowship, in the breaking of bread, and in prayers. Then fear came upon every soul, and many wonders and signs were done through the apostles. Now all who believed were together, and had all things in common.

Key Verses — Acts 2:42–44

What's It Mean?

appointed—Named, in this case, by God; see *chosen* and *elect*, which have related meanings.

chosen—As used in this lesson, *chosen* means the same as *elect*. It is used as an action verb (e.g., "God has chosen" or "many are called, but few are chosen") or as a modifier (e.g., "he is the chosen one"). We as Christians have salvation because God has chosen us.

determined—Decided authoritatively.

discrimination—In this lesson, *discrimination* means the act of treating others differently because of their class, race, or ability.

Dispersion—A scattering. The word *disperse* means "to scatter," and the Dispersion referred to in 1 Peter 1:1 was a time when Jews were scattered to the countries named.

elect—Chosen for salvation through divine mercy.

foreknowledge—God knows all things—past, present, and future. In a sense He is in the eternal now, with past, present, and future all in the present for Him. Foreknowledge is based on God's attribute of sovereignty; He determined the future, so He foreknew everything, or knew everything in advance (v. 23).

foreordained—Appointed in advance; predestined.

patriarch—One of the fathers of the Jewish people (such as David, in v. 29).

Pentecost—A name derived from the Greek word for *fifty*, the fiftieth day after the Passover, the day on which the Jews celebrated the giving of the Ten Commandments. In the first century, Jews from all over the Roman Empire made a pilgrimage to Jerusalem to celebrate the Day of Pentecost (v. 1).

predestination—The doctrine that God has determined from eternity all that will ever happen. As we have seen in the above definition, foreknowledge follows from predestination.

sovereignty—A characteristic (or attribute) of God. Simply put, it means that God determines all things and is in control of all things.

tongues—In Acts 2:3, the coming of the Holy Spirit was marked by the appearance of "tongues, as of fire" (v. 3). Here the word *tongues* seems to refer to the shape of this visible manifestation of the Spirit's coming. In verse 4, the Spirit manifested Himself in another way, by giving the apostles the ability to speak in "other tongues," or languages they did not know before.

All Right!
I read chapter 2. ☐ Yes ☐ No
☐ Yes, but I have questions.

| Date: Circa A.D. 30 | Place: Jerusalem | Roman Emperor: Tiberius | Local Ruler: Herod Antipas |

1 **What were two things that Peter and John saw as they approached the temple?** (See v. 2.)

1. _____

2. _____

Locate and highlight this gate along with Solomon's Colonnade on the drawing of Herod's temple on page 20.

2
What did the lame beggar want from Peter and John?

3
How long had he been lame? (See Acts 4:22.)

4 **Unscramble the words to find out the only thing that Peter and John had to give the lame beggar—**

eTh eNam fo usesJ shriCt = _____

5 **Write one word that tells how soon the man was healed.** _____

6 **What verse tells the man's reaction? What verbs tell what he did?**

7 **Read Acts 3:10, and complete the first two words to describe the people's reaction. Then write the first letter of each word, and notice the new word they spell.**

a_____

w_____ ⟩ ___ ___ ___

excitement

8 **Read Acts 3:12 and 3:16. In a sentence, explain the main thing Peter wanted his listeners to know.**

9 In verse 12 Peter addresses his audience as "men of Israel." **Unscramble the word to show another name for them: s w e J =** _____

He says they did four things to Jesus (vv. 13–15). **Tell what they did by drawing a line between each verb and its object:**

delivered up   the Prince of life
denied   that a murderer be released
asked   the Holy One and the Just
killed   Jesus

No doubt many of these people had been a part of the multitude in Matthew 27:15–25. **What did they say to Pilate?**

_____

What did they say in Matthew 27:25?

In Acts 3:17, Peter tells these people that what they did was done in _____.

(Exercise continues on next page.)

19

Put yourself in the sandals of the Jews who are listening to Peter. Remember, you just saw the miracle that happened to the lame man, and it caused you to realize that Jesus is God. **Would you respond to the urging of Peter in verse 19?**

☐ Yes ☐ No **If you said yes, what two things would you do?** (See v. 19.)

1.

2.

For what two reasons? (See v. 19.)

1.

2.

11 **Using the pictures as clues, complete each word to tell what Peter witnessed.**

Jesus' d_____

Jesus' b_____

Jesus' r_____

12 **Read Acts 3:22–23. What had Moses said would be the penalty for those who did not listen to "the prophet," or Christ?**

_____

10 **Fill in the words in verses 13–15 that describe Jesus.**

P R I N C E O F L I F E

Key Verse

Repent therefore and be converted, that your sins may be blotted out, so that times of refreshing may come from the presence of the Lord.

Acts 3:19

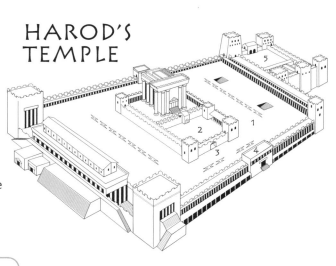

HAROD'S TEMPLE

1 Court of Gentiles
2 Court of Women
3 Beautiful Gate
4 Solomon's Colonnade
5 Fortress of Antonia

What's It Mean?

alms—Something (as money or food) given freely to relieve the poor (vv. 2–3).
blotted out—Completely wiped out (v. 19).
covenant—Solemn and binding agreement or promise (v. 25).

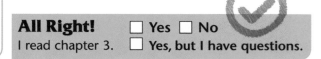

All Right! ☐ Yes ☐ No
I read chapter 3. ☐ **Yes, but I have questions.**

FROM ZEAL TO MARTYRDOM

| Date: Circa A.D. 30 | Place: Jerusalem | Roman Emperor: Tiberius | Local Ruler: Herod Antipas |

1 **Read carefully the information about various Jewish groups and offices. Beside each reference below, record any groups or offices that are included in that verse.** (Record them even when they are mentioned indirectly; for example, the council included several of them.)

Verse	Group or Office
1	
5	
6	
8	
15	
23	

2 **Why were the Sadducees greatly disturbed?** (See v. 2.)

3 Even though the apostles were taken into custody, "many of those who heard the word believed." **How many believed?**

_____

4 Verses 5 and 6 say, "On the next day,... their *rulers, elders, and scribes*" were gathered at Jerusalem with the *high priests*. **What was the group called?**

_____

5 **What did Peter want this group and all of Israel to know about the healing of the lame man?**

6 **If someone told you that it doesn't matter what you believe as long as you're sincere, what would your response be? What Scripture from chapter 4 could you use?**

7 **What impressed the council about the apostles? What did the council realize?**

22

8 **What was the council's** dilemma? (See v. 16.)

11 **Give an** example **of a time when you obeyed God rather than others.**

12 The passage in verses 24–31 is commonly called the Believer's Prayer. These verses say that certain people did "whatever Your hand and Your purpose determined before to be done." **Name the people of whom these verses speak. Answer by completing the words below.**

These could be titles, people groups, or personal names.

n_____   H_____
p_____   r_____
k_____   G_____
p_____ of l_____
P_____   P_____

9 **What did the council want to do with the name of Jesus?** (See v. 18.)

13 **We can conclude from the above passages that God is in** o t l c r o n. **Unscramble and write.**

_____

10 **In the speech balloon below,** write **in your own words Peter and John's answer to the council's request** (vv. 18–20).

14 **What** quality **did believers pray for in verse 29?**

_____

What did they get in verse 31?

_____

How were they able to have this quality?

15 Can **all** believers receive this boldness? ☐ Yes ☐ No
Write out 2 Timothy 1:7 below:

19 **Why** do you think Joses (Joseph) was also called Barnabas?

16 What number word **describes the multitude of believers?**
(See v. 32.)

_____

20 **Where** was Barnabas from?

_____

17 **What did the apostles** testify **to with great power?**
(See verse 33.)

18 When completed, the sentences in this crossword puzzle describe the early church.
Use clues **from Acts 4:32–35 to help you complete the puzzle.**

Across

3 The believers "had all things in ___."

5 "Great grace was upon them ___."

7 From time to time they ___ their land and houses.

8 They placed the proceeds "at the apostles' ___."

Down

1 The believers were of one ___.

2 They were of one ___.

4 The apostles "distributed to each as anyone had ___."

6 "Nor was there anyone among them who ___."

What's It Mean?

aristocrats—A governing class considered (usually by themselves) to be better than others.
dilemma—A situation in which a person finds that no solution is ideal.
legalism—The belief that God owes me something if I do certain things, often accompanied by the attitude that you must do it "my way" to be right with God.

Key Verse   Nor is there salvation in any other, for there is no other name under heaven given among men by which we must be saved.   Acts 4:12

All Right!
I read chapter 4.   ☐ Yes ☐ No
☐ Yes, but I have questions.

| Date: Circa A.D. 30 | Place: Jerusalem | Roman Emperor: Tiberius | Local Ruler: Herod Antipas |

 In the boxes below, Describe the story of Ananias and Sapphira in five consecutive steps. You may use words or draw pictures.

2 **How does this story compare with the story of Barnabas in 4:36–37?**

Similarities

Differences

1

2

3

4

5

3 **Did the couple die because they held back part of the money from the sale of the property?** ☐ Yes ☐ No **Explain why you think they died.**

4 Does **God deal the same today with people who lie about their giving?** ☐ Yes ☐ No **Why or why not?**

5 In verse 3 Peter says Satan filled Ananias' heart, so we know that Satan was active in the world at the time of the early church. **Is Satan still active in today's world?** ☐ Yes ☐ No If you are a Christian, you are probably careful about what books and magazines you read, what movies and videos you watch, and what Internet sites you visit. Examine your life to be sure you aren't allowing Satan to have his way in your life. **In the back of your workbook, write a prayer to God related to this.**

6 **What did the entire church feel as a result of this incident?** (See vv. 5 and 11.)

_____

Who else felt the same emotion?

_____

26

7 **How might you have felt if you had been standing in that room with Peter?**

8 Did **the deaths of Ananias and Sapphira cause division or unity in the church?** (See v. 12.) ☐ Division ☐ Unity

9 Read verses 13–14 carefully. Verse 13 says, "None of the rest dared join them," yet verse 14 says, "And believers were increasingly added to the Lord, multitudes of both men and women." **Is there a contradiction here? Explain the answer to this possible problem found in the Bible.**

10 In verse 20 the angel of the Lord told the apostles to speak "to the people all the words of this life." **What were those words?**

11 **Unscramble the letters below and form a word that describes the apostles in verse 25.** (Also read verses 28 and 29.)

b o d i n e t e = _____

12 **Who made up the council in verse 27?** (Look back to chapter 4.)

G	A	S	I	G	N	S	S
H	A	L	I	Q	F	P	W
E	D	T	L	C	I	W	O
A	D	W	H	R	K	A	D
L	E	O	I	E	Q	F	A
E	D	T	C	P	R	G	H
D	S	S	D	E	B	E	S
S	R	E	D	N	O	W	D

PUZZLER
13 Circle or highlight eight words that best describe the happenings in Acts 5:12–16.

14 Write **what Peter said in verse 29.**

What **verse** in chapter 4 is very similar?

15 When Peter stated in verse 31, "Him God has exalted to His right hand to be Prince and Savior, to give repentance to Israel and forgiveness of sins," he is saying, in **essence,** that Jesus is

_____

16 Keeping question 15 in mind, **what made the council so furious that they wanted to kill them?** (Read v. 30.)

17 Complete **the list of facts about Gamaliel by filling in the blanks below from Acts 5:34:**

a. He was a _____.

b. He was a teacher of the _____.

c. He was _____ by all the people.

And from Acts 22:3:

d. He was _____ teacher.

Then Peter and the other apostles answered and said, "We ought to obey God rather than men."

Key Verse   Acts 5:29

18 Quote **a portion of Gamaliel's speech that we should always remember.** (See Acts 5:38–39.) "And now I say to you,

19 R**eflect on verses 38 and 39, and then think about what you want to do most in life. Check the appropriate box: Is it ☐ "of God" or ☐ "of men"? In the back of your workbook, write a paragraph to God about your main goal in life.**

20 In the back of your workbook, **describe in detail how the apostles reacted to this persecution. Consider both verses 41 and 42 in your answer.**

What's It Mean?

beaten—A form of punishment used among the Hebrews consisting of blows to the back with a rod. (See 2 Corinthians 11:24.)

couches—As used in verse 15, mats that are used to lie down on.

doctrine—The things that are taught and are believed as the truths of God's Word.

indignation—Anger or jealousy (v. 17).

All Right! ☐ Yes ☐ No
I read chapter 5. ☐ Yes, but I have questions.

27

| Date: Circa A.D. 35 | Place: Jerusalem | Roman Emperor: Tiberius | Local Ruler: Herod Antipas |

1 DIGGING DEEPER

We see in Acts 6:1 the word *disciples* used for the second of many times in Acts. **What is the difference between a disciple and an apostle?** Find each verse in Acts and summarize what it says about disciples or apostles.

Disciples

1:15

6:1

6:2

6:7

Apostles

1:2

1:21 –26

4:33

6:2

Study the above information carefully. What is the difference between disciples and apostles?

2 What was the complaint given by the Hellenists?

3 According to verse 2, what problem were the twelve trying to solve?

4 What three job requirements did the apostles give for the seven? They must

1. have a good _____

2. be full of _____

3. be filled with _____

5 What two things would these new workers enable the disciples to devote themselves to?

1. _____

2. _____

28

Are all apostles disciples? ☐ Yes ☐ No
Are all disciples apostles? ☐ Yes ☐ No

So many disciples, so little time!

6 **What people in your church have responsibilities that enable your pastor to devote much of his time to the Word and to prayer?** To find the answer, you might want to talk to an adult member.

Laying On of Hands

In Acts 6, the laying on of the apostles' hands signifies a commissioning. The apostles commissioned the seven to the responsibility of caring for the physical needs of the church. (Though not called that, these seven men were the church's first deacons.) Later in Acts 13:3 we see the laying of hands on Paul and Barnabas as they are commissioned to the foreign mission field. Laying on of hands was done in blessings, healings, and the giving of the power of the Holy Spirit.

7 **According to verses 5 and 8, what kind of man was Stephen?**

Where did Stephen get his power?

_____

8 **List the chosen seven. Circle two you are most familiar with.**

1. _____   5. _____
2. _____   6. _____
3. _____   7. _____
4. _____

10 Recalling the information about the priests in chapter 4, consider what will happen when they become believers. **Why will they have a significant part in spreading the gospel?**

11 **What did Stephen do among the people?**

_____

9 **What three things happened as a result of appointing these men to this work?** (See v. 7.)

1.

2.

3.

12 **Tell how Acts 6:10 is a fulfillment of Luke 21:12–15.**

29

13 **What was the** conspiracy **against Stephen?**

He was brought before what?

14 **Why do you think Stephen's face was "as the face of an angel"?** (See v. 15.)

 Key Verse

And the word of God spread, and the number of the disciples multiplied greatly in Jerusalem, and a great many of the priests were obedient to the faith.

Acts 6:7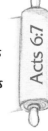

15 We learn more about Stephen, one of the seven, in verses 8 through 15. **Complete the crisscross puzzle with the six nouns below, which tell about Stephen's deeds, qualities, and appearance.**

| angel | signs | wisdom |
| faith | spirit | wonders |

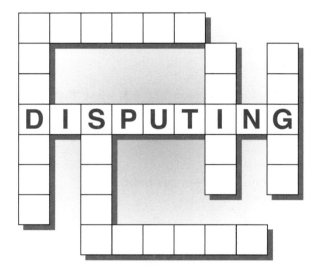

D I S P U T I N G

What's It Mean?

blasphemous—Speaking evil against God (vv. 11, 13).
commissioning—Giving a person the power and authority to do a job.
conspiracy—A plan of evil against somebody.
Hellenists—In Acts 6, Jewish Christians who spoke Greek and had adopted the Greek culture (v. 1).
induced—Caused to happen; convinced (v. 11).

All Right! ☐ Yes ☐ No
I read chapter 6. ☐ Yes, but I have questions.

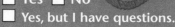

| Date: Circa A.D. 35 | Place: Jerusalem | Roman Emperor: Tiberius | Local Ruler: Herod Antipas |

1 In the first 50 verses of Acts 7, Stephen preaches to the council, giving them a brief overview of the history of the Hebrew nation. Solve the crossword below to identify several key characters named in Stephen's message.

Across

1 He sent his sons to find grain in Egypt.
2 He built the temple, a house for God.
5 He was the father of Jacob.
6 "And God gave him no inheritance in [the land], not even enough to set his foot on."
8 He, not Moses, finally took possession of the land.

Down

1 "God was with him … and gave him favor and wisdom in the presence of Pharaoh."
3 He "was learned in all the wisdom of the Egyptians, and was mighty in words and deeds."
4 He "asked to find a dwelling for the God of Jacob," but his son built the temple.
7 He helped make a calf so that the Israelites could worship it.

2 As Stephen opens his message, what does he call the people he is addressing? (Read v. 2.)

_____

3 Verse 6 says the Hebrews lived in a foreign land and were in bondage for 400 years. What was the land, and to whom were they in bondage?

_____

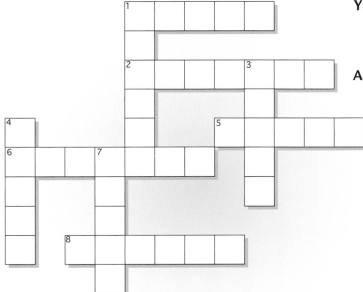

SOLVE THE MYSTERY

4 How old was Moses when he died? To figure this out, add how old he was when he left Egypt to how long he was gone before he returned to how long he was in the wilderness. All these figures are found in Stephen's message. After figuring this up, compare your total to Moses' age when he died (Deuteronomy 34:7).

Age when he left Egypt _____

Years gone before return _____

Years in the wilderness _____

Total _____

Age in Deuteronomy 34:7 _____

5 According to verses 48 and 49, where does God dwell, and where does He not dwell?

He dwells in _____.

He does *not* dwell in _____

_____.

31

6 List **six things Stephen said that made the Council angry, including** three **things he called them and** three **things he accused them of doing or failing to do.**

He called them

1.

2.

3.

He said they had

1.

2.

3.

7 **Was the Holy Spirit** active **in the lives of the** Old Testament **people?** Prove **and explain your answer using Scripture.** (Read v. 51 carefully.)

32

8 Describe **in** five steps **the events from verses 54 through 60.**

1.

2.

3.

4.

5.

9 Study **verses 59–60 carefully and** compare **them with Luke 23:34 and 23:46. Make a** comment **concerning the relationship found in these passages.**

10 In 1 Peter 4 the author talks about living and suffering because of our Christian walk. **After reading** Acts 7:55–60 **carefully,** write **the verses of this passage that fit the 1 Peter 4 verses below:**

1 Peter 4:13b:

1 Peter 4:12:

1 Peter 4:11a:

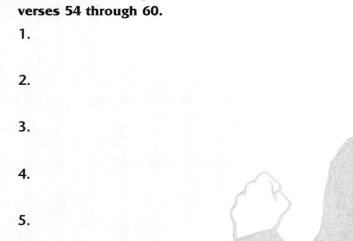

11 Draw **a picture of the man mentioned in verse 59 and a picture of the man mentioned in Acts 7:58 and 8:1.**

12 At **whose feet did the witnesses lay their outer garments?**

_____

Key Verses

And they stoned Stephen as he was calling on God and saying, "Lord Jesus, receive my spirit." Then he knelt down and cried out with a loud voice, "Lord, do not charge them with this sin." And when he had said this, he fell asleep.

Acts 7:59–60

What's It Mean?

begot—Fathered, or became the father of (v. 8).

oracles—Words from God spoken through a person (v. 38; see also 1 Peter 4:11a).

patriarchs—Fathers of a particular family or nation (v. 9).

stoning—A common form of capital punishment in biblical times. Large stones were thrown on the victim, usually until he or she died (vv. 58–59).

uncircumcised in heart—Impure and disobedient before God (v. 51).

MEDITATION

Reflect on Stephen's life and death. **Write a conversation you might have with God about this event.**

All Right! ☐ Yes ☐ No
I read chapter 7. ☐ Yes, but I have questions.

33

· PETER'S VISION ·

FROM JERUSALEM TO THE ENDS OF THE EARTH

| Date: Circa A.D. 35 | Place: Jerusalem | Roman Emperor: Tiberius | Local Ruler: Herod Antipas |

1 **What three things did Saul do, according to the first three verses of chapter 8?**

1.

2.

3.

5 The early Christians were witnesses first to those closest to them, then to those farther away. It should be no different now. **Prayerfully think of five people around you that you could be a witness to. After you have made your list, pray for them.**

1.

2.

3.

4.

5.

2 **Why do you think the church scattered?**

6 **What action word is the key word in verse 4?**

_____

3 **Unscramble the words to find out who we know stayed behind:**

het patessol = _____

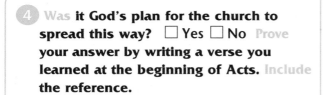

7 **Verse 5 says Philip went down to Samaria, which is north of Jerusalem. How could he go down when he went north?**

4 **Was it God's plan for the church to spread this way?** ☐ Yes ☐ No Prove **your answer by writing a verse you learned at the beginning of Acts.** Include **the reference.**

8 Complete **the sentences showing what Philip accomplished in Samaria.**

Unclean spirits came out of those who

_____.

Many who were paralyzed and lame

_____.

And the people in that city felt

_____.

36

Samaritans were an Israelite sect that rejected Jerusalem as the center of worship and built their own temple on Mount Gerizim near Samaria. They believed in the Pentateuch but rejected the rest of the Old Testament. They were despised by the Jews and were considered compromising half-breeds. Traveling in Samaria and associating with Samaritans was unacceptable for Jews.

9 Consider the information about the Samaritans; did Philip take a big step by presenting the gospel to the Samaritans? ☐ Yes ☐ No Explain your answer.

 DIGGING  DEEPER

10 According to Romans 8:9, who is supposed to be in control of us as believers? _____

Romans 8:9 strongly supports that God the Father, God the Son, and God the Holy Spirit are one (the Trinity). Explain how this passage supports the Trinity.

Keeping Romans 8:9 in mind, if the Samaritans in Acts 8:9–14 were Christians, why had they not received the Holy Spirit? (See vv. 15–17.)

11 Describe Simon the sorcerer in your own words. (See vv. 9–11.)

12 What was Simon the sorcerer's evil request? _____

13 What was Peter's reaction?

Why did Peter react harshly?

37

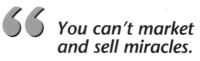
You can't market and sell miracles.
—Mark Landess

14 Do you believe Simon was truly a believer? ☐ Yes ☐ No Give good reasons for your answer!

18 The Ethiopian had questions about Isaiah 53:7–8. How would you have explained these verses? (Acts 8:32–33, quoted from Isaiah.)
Isaiah 53:7 was fulfilled by Jesus, who

Isaiah 53:8 was fulfilled when

15 Who was Philip? (See Acts 6:5.)

19 Skim through Isaiah 53 and write out on the scroll portions of other passages that Philip might have explained.

16 Read carefully verses 26–40. Was Philip guided by the Spirit? ☐ Yes ☐ No Write out portions of two verses (with references) that verify your answer.
    1.

    2.

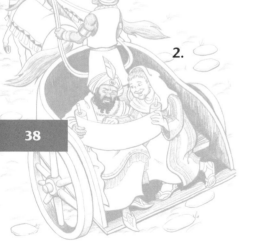

17 How did God work in the life of the Ethiopian before he met Philip?

Baptism

The New Testament knows nothing of a disciple who wasn't baptized. Baptism does not save us, but it is a step of obedience and a demonstration to others of our commitment to Christ. Because of the life-changing impact of Christ, most people in the early church wanted to be baptized immediately after they became believers.

20 **What three things did Philip do in his personal evangelism that we could do when we witness?**

1.

2.

3.

21 **How important was baptism to the Ethiopian?** _____

22 **Did his baptism come before or after his belief?** ☐ Before ☐ After
Write the verse that proves this.

23 Underline **the part of Matthew 28:19 that has been** accomplished **in the story of Philip and the Ethiopian.**

"Go therefore and make disciples of all the nations, baptizing them in the name of the Father and of the Son and of the Holy Spirit."

Key Verse

Therefore those who were scattered went everywhere preaching the word.

Acts 8:4

24 Solve **the** cryptogram **to determine the** declaration **of the Ethiopian (v. 37) and the** realization **of Simon the sorcerer (vv. 9–25).**

Each letter of the cryptogram represents another letter of the alphabet. Letters are grouped into words. It is best to start with the shorter words. Use a pencil to write the correct letters under the code letters. Each code letter represents the same other letter throughout the puzzle. (If *O* represents *E*, then all the *O*'s in the puzzle represent *E*'s.

A Declaration of the Ethiopian

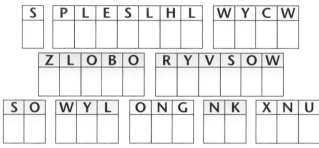

S	P	L	E	S	L	H	L		W	Y	C	W

Z	L	O	B	O		R	Y	V	S	O	W

S	O		W	Y	L		O	N	G		N	K		X	N	U

A Realization of Simon the Sorcerer

M	N	B		R	C	G	'W		P	B	M		W	Y	L

O	Q	S	V	S	W		N	K		X	N	U

What's It Mean?

evangelism—In the context of Christianity, telling others about Christ.
havoc—Confusion and destruction (v. 3).
heed—To listen to or obey (v. 6).
lamentation—Mourning or grieving, often loudly (v. 2).
Pentateuch—The first five books of the Old Testament.
sorcery—The practice of black magic.

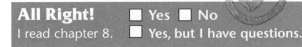

All Right! ☐ Yes ☐ No
I read chapter 8. ☐ Yes, but I have questions.

39

| Date: Circa A.D. 35 | Place: Damascas, Jerusalem, Tarsus, Lydda, Joppa | Roman Emperor: Tiberius | Local Ruler: Herod Antipas |

1 Who were the people of "the Way" mentioned in verse 2?

_____

2 What was Saul planning to do when the Lord spoke to him?

3 What part did Ananias play in Saul's life?

4 Carefully read verses 9–12. Beside the proper pictures below tell what Saul was doing for the three days he was blind.

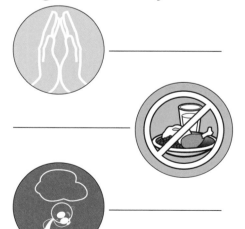

_____

_____

_____

5 In verses 13–14 we see Ananias complaining about the task God wants him to do. What is the first word of God's reply?

_____

6 In verses 15–16, find and list three things that God says to Ananias about Saul's future.

7 Unscramble a word that indicates how soon God healed Saul through Ananias.

y d e e m i m a l i t = _____

Miraculous healings in the Bible were always instant and complete.

8 At what point in this story do you think Saul is born again? Explain your answer.

9 **Read verses 20–23 carefully, and list below how Saul now compares with Stephen as seen back in Acts 6:9–15. Write out a phrase from Acts 9:20–23 that matches each verse listed below from chapter 6.**

Chapter 6, verse 8: "Stephen, full of faith and power …"

Chapter 6, verses 9 and 10: "Then there arose some from what is called the Synagogue of the Freedmen,… disputing with Stephen. And they were not able to resist the wisdom and the Spirit by which he spoke."

Chapter 6, verse 11: "Then they secretly induced men to say, 'We have heard him speak blasphemous words against Moses and God.'"

If Stephen had not died, Paul might not have lived!

10 **Describe Saul's witness in Damascus. Check the proper boxes.**
☐ Bold ☐ Powerful ☐ Weak ☐ Ineffective

11 Verse 23 says "after many days were past." Read Galatians 1:15–17, and tell where Saul was during those "many days."

_____

According to Galatians 1:18, how long was the time span between Saul's salvation and his trip to Jerusalem?

_____

12 **What would verse 25 seem to indicate about Saul's size?**

_____

13 **Read verse 26. Do you blame the disciples for their reaction to Saul?**
☐ Yes ☐ No Explain your answer.

14 **Who comes as an encouraging helper for Saul?**

_____

Why is this not surprising?

15 Why do you think Saul had to be especially **bold** in Jerusalem?

16 Considering all that has happened so far in this chapter, **why** did Jerusalem believers now enjoy a time of peace as described in verse 31?

17 Complete the quotation from verse 31 to explain why the church multiplied.

Because they were "walking in the

_____ and in the

_____ .

18 Unscramble the word below that tells how soon God healed Aeneas through Peter.
e a l t i m i m y d e =

_____

19 What was the **result** of Aeneas' healing? (See v. 35.)

20 Describe the **character** of Dorcas. (See vv. 36 and 39.)

21 What was the **result** of the **raising** of **Dorcas?** (See v. 42.)

_____

22 Dorcas is remembered as one who used her time, talent (ability), and treasure (possessions) to minister to others. **Describe one way you could use each—your time, talent, and treasure—to help those around you.**

Time:

Talent:

Treasure:

42

Did you know?   *Tabitha* (Aramaic) and *Dorcas* (Greek) both mean *"gazelle."*

23 **Who** does Peter stay with in Joppa?

_____

24 **After reading the information below about tanners,** explain the significance of Peter's stay with Simon the tanner.

Tanners

Tanners are those who prepare animal hides for use (in a process called *tanning*). The main product is leather. Tanners were considered lowly by the Jews since they dealt with dead and unclean animals, and the materials used for tanning had a strong odor. Dog dung was sometimes used in the tanning process. Because they were considered unclean, tanners had to live outside the towns, often near water.

25 This crisscross puzzle contains words found in the story about the raising of Dorcas. **Solve** the puzzle by simply placing the words in the boxes provided. Each word fits in one specific row.

died   alive   deeds   prayed
good   Peter   Dorcas   widows
weeping

B E L I E V E D

What's It Mean?

edified—In a biblical context, instructed in spiritual matters through the study of God's Word and the teaching of others (v. 31).

goads—Long, pointed sticks used for guiding oxen (v. 5).

Hellenist—In chapter 9, Jews who adopted the Greek language and many Greek ideas (v. 29).

imploring—Pleading with someone to do something (v. 38).

Key Verse

Then the churches throughout all Judea, Galilee, and Samaria had peace and were edified. And walking in the fear of the Lord and in the comfort of the Holy Spirit, they were multiplied.

Acts 9:31

All Right!
I read chapter 9.
☐ Yes ☐ No
☐ Yes, but I have questions.

43

| Date: Circa A.D. 38 | Place: Joppa, Caesarea | Roman Emperor: Caligula | Local Ruler: Herodians (Antipas and Agrippa I) |

1 **List six facts about Cornelius.**

1. c_____
2. d_____
3. f_____ G_____
4. g_____ g_____
5. p_____ a_____
6. g_____ r_____

2 At the beginning of chapter 10, we see that God is working in the lives of Peter and Cornelius at the same time. Below are boxes representing the progressive steps for both of their stories. **Check each verse reference and then write a brief statement in each box describing each step.**

Cornelius' Story

> v. 3

> v. 9a

> v. 17b

> v. 18

Peter's Story

> Peter is lodging in the house of Simon the tanner.

> vv. 9b–16

> v. 17a

> vv. 19–20

Peter and Cornelius' Story

> vv. 21–23

> vv. 24–25

3 The Jews often divided the day into the third, sixth, and ninth hours, beginning at 6:00 AM. **What time would the** sixth **hour of verse 9 and the** ninth **hour of verse 3 be?**

3rd hour is 9:00 AM	6th hour is	9th hour is

4 **What was God's purpose in the vision He gave Peter?** (See v. 28.)

9 **What had God shown Peter in this story?**

5 **Who went with Peter to see Cornelius?**

_____

How many went? (See 11:12.) _____

6 **Was Cornelius expecting something special to happen when Peter arrived?** ☐ Yes ☐ No **Explain your answer.**

10 **Why are verses 34–35 important to you? Why are these verses important to the world? Answer in the boxes below.**

YOU

WORLD

7 **Why was Peter's step into Cornelius' house a big step?** (See v. 28.)

11 **Is there a condition for God's acceptance of a person?** ☐ Yes ☐ No **Support your answer with a quotation from the Scripture you just read.**

8 **Unscramble the letters and fill in the blank boxes to determine whom God accepts.**

A	L	L	O	W	W	H	A	T	E	A	R	R	I	G	H	A	D
	D		H	O		F		I	S		H	I	M		T	N	

12 **What two major events had Peter and his companions witnessed?** (See vv. 39–41.)

1. _____

2. _____

13 **Write a verse from this chapter that shows the** importance **of the name of Christ. Include the reference.**

14 **Why were those Jews who came with Peter** astonished?

15 **According to Peter in Acts 11:17, how did the Gentiles' receiving the Holy Spirit** compare **with the apostles' experience in chapter 2?**

_____

16 Explain **why Peter said,** *"Can anyone forbid water, that these should not be baptized?"*

Remember: The New Testament knows nothing of a disciple who has not been baptized. Baptism does not save a believer, but it serves as an outward sign of the inward reality.

46

17 Peter's experience in Cornelius' home is a good example of a home Bible study. Below are some sentences describing seven Bible study characteristics shown in Acts 10. **Complete the sentences using the words below.**

1. The meeting was all _____ by God.
2. It took place in a _____.
3. They met on common _____.
4. There was a _____ group of people.
5. Many _____ were asked.
6. The _____ was taught.
7. People were _____ to respond.

gospel   asked

home   ground   directed

questions   large

What's It Mean?

centurion—A Roman officer in charge of 100 men (v. 1).

Gentiles—"Heathen" or "non-Jewish" (v. 45); the word no longer carries the negative meaning "heathen," as it did to Jews in the time of Acts. The Greek word *ethnos* suggests its current meaning, "anyone who is not a Jew." (The same root is found in the word *ethnic*.)

Key Verses

Then Peter opened his mouth and said: "In truth I perceive that God shows no partiality. But in every nation whoever fears Him and works righteousness is accepted by Him."

Acts 10:34–35

All Right!   ☐ Yes ☐ No
I read chapter 10.   ☐ Yes, but I have questions.

Date: A.D. 38–43, 46	Place: Jerusalem, Antioch	Emperor: Caligula, Claudius	Local Ruler: Herodians (Antipas and Agrippa I)

1 Why did those of the circumcision (Jewish believers) **contend** with Peter?

Circumcised men (Jews) To the Jews, circumcision was symbolic of the covenant between God and their nation; thus, in this context, circumcised men were Jews or, as used in chapter 11, Jewish believers. The phrase often describes the Jewish Christian sect that regarded obedience to the Jewish law as necessary for salvation.

Uncircumcised men (Non-Jews) Often they are referred to as Greeks, gentiles, or pagans.

2 How did Peter **explain** what had happened to him at the home of Cornelius? (See v. 4.)

3 In verses 5–17 Peter recounts his experience with Cornelius. **How close is his story in this chapter to that of chapter 10?**

4 Compare **verse 14 to Acts 10:6. What** additional **information do you learn in verse 14?**

5 According to verse 15, how did the Holy Spirit's coming on Cornelius compare with His coming on the apostles?

6 According to verse 17, when did people receive **the gift of the Holy Spirit?**

7 If you are not **a Jew, which verse in this section may be the most significant to you?** Write **the verse out.**

8 Quote a prophetic **verse in Acts 1 that is being fulfilled in Acts 11:19.**

Did you know?   Antioch of Syria was the third largest city in the Roman Empire.

9 Solve the cryptograms below to see what the church in Antioch was like. Read the instructions on how to solve cryptograms in chapter 8. Below are three statements about the Antioch church. The letters are the same for all three statements. Studying Acts chapter 11 will help you.

Q	C	X	A		Y	N		F	Q	S		H	Y	B	A

M	C	G		M	W	F	Q		F	Q	S	U

C		P	B	S	C	F		X	D	U	L	S	B

F	D	B	X	S	A		F	Y

F	Q	S		H	Y	B	A

G	Q	Y	M	S	A		F	Q	S

P	B	C	E	S		Y	N		P	Y	A

10 When Barnabas arrived at the Antioch church, what **did he do immediately?** (See v. 23.)

Does this surprise you?
☐ Yes ☐ No **Explain.**

11 List **three** things you could do **right now** to encourage others.

1. _____

2. _____

3. _____

12 What would Barnabas be like if he were **alive** today? **Describe in** detail **what he might be doing, what his personality might be like, what his home might be like, etc.**

13 Who else in Acts was like **Barnabas?** Unscramble the letters.

teeSnph = _____

(Read v. 24, and then Acts 6:5.)

14 Why do you think Saul was in Tarsus? (See Acts 22:3.)

15 How long did they **teach** in Antioch?

_____

16 What are the believers in Antioch called for the first time?

_____

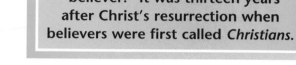

The word *Christian* means, in a sense, "Christ follower" or "believer." It was thirteen years after Christ's resurrection when believers were first called *Christians*.

17 Who was Agabus?

18 Answer the following questions to describe the first recorded Christian mission relief effort.

Why was the relief needed?

Who sent the relief?

How did they give?

To whom was the gift sent?

19 Who delivered these gifts?

_____

Key Verses

"If therefore God gave them the same gift as He gave us when we believed on the Lord Jesus Christ, who was I that I could withstand God?" When they heard these things they became silent; and they glorified God, saying, "Then God has also granted to the Gentiles repentance to life."

Acts 11:17–18

49

What's It Mean?

contend—To fight or argue with another.

All Right! I read chapter 11. ☐ Yes ☐ No ☐ Yes, but I have questions.

| Date: A.D. 44 | Place: Jerusalem, Antioch | Roman Emperor: Claudius | Local Ruler: Herod Agrippa I |

Note: This is a step back in time from the famine relief of chapter 11.

1 What happened to James, and why?

Did you know?

Killed with the sword means to be beheaded.

2 What were the Jews hoping for when Herod imprisoned Peter? (See v. 11.)

_____

3 James and John are the sons of Zebedee. Read **Matthew 20:20–23, and explain how James' death is the partial fulfillment of Christ's words.** Keep in mind that when Christ says "drink the same cup" He is referring to the cup of death.

4 What were the Days of Unleavened Bread? (See v. 4.)

_____

Passover At this time it was a weeklong celebration of the deliverance of Israel from bondage in Egypt. The name *Passover* originated when the angel of death "passed over" the homes of those who followed God's instructions, putting the blood of a sacrificed lamb on the doorposts of their houses.

5 What kind of prayer did the church offer on Peter's behalf?

_____

6 This crossword puzzle is made up of words from the story of Peter's escape from prison. **Use the clues below and Acts 12:4–11 to help you complete the puzzle.**

Across
2 Fell off of Peter
6 The number of squads guarding Peter
7 Was offered up while Peter was in prison

Down
1 Peter thought he was seeing this
3 Led Peter out of prison
4 Put Peter in prison
5 Opened of its own accord
7 Herod intended to execute him next

7 Read Colossians 4:10. How is **John Mark** related to Barnabas? _____

Read Acts 12:12. How is Barnabas related to **Mary?** _____

8 Place yourself in Rhoda's sandals. How would you have **reacted** to seeing Peter?

9 Considering verses 5 and 12, what is so **wonderful** about Peter's deliverance?

10 How do you see **lack of faith** in those who were praying for Peter's release?

How did they **feel** when they saw Peter? (See v. 16.)

How does this **challenge** you in your prayer life?

DIGGING DEEPER

12 Read verse 19 to answer the following: How **seriously** must a Roman guard have taken his job, and **why?**

How is this information **helpful** in defending the fact of the **resurrection** (as opposed to the lie of the Jews in Matthew 28:11–15)**?**

11 **Quote** the part of verse 17 that tells us we are to **share** with others what God has done.

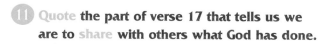

Eaten by Worms?

According to Josephus (a famous historian of the time), Herod died after five days of violent pains in his "belly." Whether this was from parasitic worms or some disease is not known.

13 **Why did Herod die?**

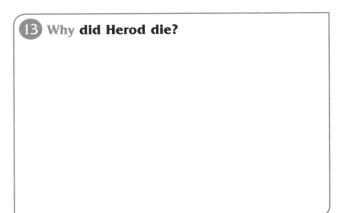

14 **What two verbs tell what happened to the Word of God after Herod's death?** (See v. 24.)

_____ and _____

15 **Who do Barnabas and Saul take with them on their return trip from Jerusalem?** (Write his full name, with his surname in capital letters.)

_____

16 **Who is John Mark's mother?**

_____

What's It Mean?

gird—To put on and secure your clothing (v. 8).
harass—To persecute or pick on (v. 1).
oration—A speech (v. 21).
squad—A small unit of four soldiers (v. 4).
surname—The name borne in common by members of a family (v. 12).

Key Verse

But the word of God grew and multiplied.

Acts 12:24

All Right!   ☐ Yes ☐ No
I read chapter 10. ☐ Yes, but I have questions.

MISSIONARY JOURNEY ONE AND JERUSALEM COUNCIL

Date: A.D. 46–47	Place: Antioch Syria, Pisidian Antioch	Roman Emperor: Claudius	Local Ruler: Various

1 What was interesting about Manaen?

2 What were the prophets and teachers doing when God called Paul and Barnabas for the first missionary trip?

3 Quote portions of two verses that tell us Paul and Barnabas were directed on this mission by the Holy Spirit.

v. 2:

v. 4:

4 After arriving at Salamis, where did Paul and Barnabas preach?

5 Who went as Saul and Barnabas' helper? Include his surname mentioned in Acts 12:12.

6 What very serious mistake did Elymas the sorcerer make?

7 What CHANGE do we see in verse 9?

8 Complete the passages below that were Paul's description of Elymas.

full of all

full of all

son of the

enemy of all

was perverting the

9 Examine your life carefully and be honest with yourself. Are you guilty of any of these things that Paul accused Elymas of?

10 Describe the similarities and differences between Elymas' and Saul's blindness:

Similarities

Differences

11 **What did** Sergius Paulus **think about the "the teachings of the Lord"?**

12 **What** happened **to Paul and Barnabas' helper John Mark?**

13 **To whom, besides the Jews, did Paul** address **his message?**

14 The anagram below is drawn from Paul's message at the synagogue of Pisidian Antioch as found in verses 17–25. Read **through this passage and study the clues below.** Unscramble **each word and write it on the line.**

coshe	"The God of this people _____ our fathers."
dalteex	God _____ the people when they were strangers in Egypt.
yortf	The children of Israel were in the wilderness _____ years.
sudjeg	The _____ ruled Israel for 450 years.
aulS	_____ was the first king of Israel.
daDvi	_____ was a man after God's own heart.
viroSa	God raised up a _____ for Israel.
partenence	John's baptism was a baptism of _____.

Pisidian Antioch

Pisidian Antioch needs to be distinguished from Antioch of Syria, where Paul and Barnabas were commissioned (and where believers were first called *Christians*). Even though it was a crossroads city near the region of Pisidia, it was small compared with the great metropolis of Antioch, Syria.

15 **To** whom **did Paul say the message of salvation has been sent?** (See v. 26.)

_____ of the _____ of _____ and those among them _____, showing that the message had come to both _____ and _____.

16 **How often is the** resurrection **mentioned between verses 30 and 37?**
Circle one: **1   2   3   4   5   6   7**
What does this indicate **about the resurrection?**

_____

17 **Paul quotes Psalm 16:10.** (See v. 35.) Who else **quoted this same passage in a sermon in Acts?** (Read Acts 2:27.)

_____

18 Read **verses 38 and 39. Use** two key words **you read that tell something important about all believers.**

1. Believers have _____.
2. Believers are _____.

55

19 **What word indicates the Gentiles had a great desire to hear the Word of God the next Sabbath?**

Do you have this same desire for the Word of God?
☐ Yes ☐ No

20 **From Scripture, what was the response to Paul's message after the congregation left?**

What was the response of the city on the next Sabbath?

21 **You have seen Saul's name changed to Paul. Read verses 43b and 46a carefully, and compare them with verses 2b and 7b. Examine these verses in detail, and see whether you can discover something else that has changed. Write it below.**

22 **What new direction do you see in verses 46 and 47?**

Why? (Look back at Acts 9:15.)

23 **Read verse 48a. Is this verse important to you?** ☐ Yes ☐ No **Why?**

DIGGING   DEEPER

24 Read verse 48 carefully, and use it to answer the questions below.

Is our salvation determined ahead of time by God? ☐ Yes ☐ No

Do we choose to accept Christ or not?
☐ Yes ☐ No

Thoroughly explain why you answered the way you did. Don't ignore what God's Word says in verse 48!

25 **Name the region where the Word of the Lord was being spread (verse 49). Be sure to look it up on your map.**

_____

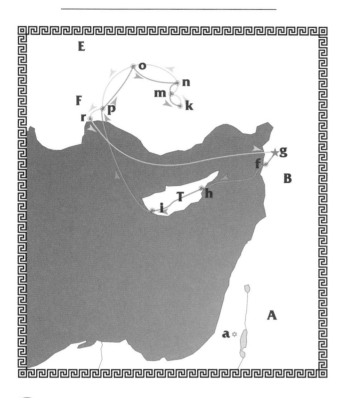

26 **Match the letters on the map with corresponding place names below.**

____ Antioch	____ Paphos
____ Attalia	____ Perga
____ Derbe	____ Pisidian Antioch
____ Iconium	____ Salamis
____ Lystra	____ Seleucia
____ Pamphylia	

Key Verses

Therefore let it be known to you, brethren, that through this Man is preached to you the forgiveness of sins; and by Him everyone who believes is justified from all things from which you could not be justified by the law of Moses.

Acts 13:38–39

What's It Mean?

appointed—Assigned to a position (v. 48).

contradicting—Going against (v. 45).

corruption—Decay (vv. 34–37).

devout—Loyal to a person or a cause (v. 50).

justified—In the biblical sense, being justified consists of two parts: being made free from any penalty, and receiving all the benefits of one who has obeyed the law (v. 39).

proconsul—Governor of a province (v. 7 and Acts 18:12).

proselytes—New converts to Judaism (v. 43).

Body Language

"They shook off the dust from their feet" (Acts 13:51). This was a visual display signifying they were no longer responsible to God for the souls of those who rejected them.

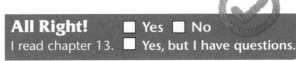

All Right! ▢ Yes ▢ No
I read chapter 13. ▢ Yes, but I have questions.

57

| Date: A.D. 47–Mid 48 | Place: Iconium, Derbe, Antioch | Roman Emperor: Claudius | Local Ruler: Various |

1 **What did Paul and Barnabas usually do first when they entered a new city?**

2 **What people were saved at Iconium? Complete the sentence.**
"A great multitude both of the _____ and of the _____ believed."

3 **What did the unbelieving Jews do to the Gentiles?** (See v. 2.)

4 **Paul and Barnabas stayed a long time in Iconium. What did they do while they were there?** (See v. 3.)

5 **What evil plot was attempted against Paul and Barnabas?**

6 **What is the gospel they preached?** (See v. 7.)

7 **Read verse 10 and then Acts 3:8. What two actions do these verses have in common?**
_____ and _____

SOLVE THE ANALOGY

8 Paul was the main speaker, and Barnabas was the larger in size of the two. In Greek mythology Zeus was the ruler of the gods, and Hermes was his messenger. **Thus the Lycians believed Paul was _____ and Barnabas was _____.**

Zeus and Hermes

Zeus (the Roman god Jupiter) was the king of all the Greek gods. He always carried a thunderbolt and is sometimes called the thunder god. Hermes (the Roman god Mercury) was Zeus' messenger. He is often pictured with wings on his feet.

At **Lystra** there was a temple to Zeus. The people of Lystra believed that Zeus and Hermes had visited an old couple there and had left without any other recognition. They were determined that this would never happen again.

9 **Using the information above, explain why the events of verses 8–18 occurred.**

10 Herod was called a god (Acts 12), and now Paul is called a god. Compare these events, listing both similarities and differences.

Similarities

Differences

It is believed that **Lystra** was the home of Timothy and that he became a believer as a result of Paul's ministry there. See 2 Timothy 3:10–11.

13 Why did the people who thought Paul was a god end up stoning him?

14 Study 20–21. Was this a miracle?
☐ Yes ☐ No Why do you think so?

Common Grace

In verse 17 we see an example of common grace—God's blessing on everyone, believers and unbelievers alike. Common grace is not to be confused with the saving grace given to those who have trusted Christ (1 Corinthians 1:4–5).

11 Why did Paul and Barnabas tear their perfectly good clothing?

15 What city did they go to next?

16 Read Acts 20:4 and name a Christian brother who lived in that city.

12 Paul says in verse 15 that you should turn from "vain things." What things did he mean for the people of Lystra? What are some useless things that a young person today should turn from?

59

17 The verbs in the crisscross puzzle tell how Paul and Barnabas, on their return trip, ministered to the churches at Lystra, Iconium, and Antioch. **Solve the puzzle by simply placing the words below in the boxes provided. Each word fits into a specific row or column.**

exhorting
appointed
prayed
fasted
commended

STRENGTHENING

"A long time"
The term *a long time* in verse 28 was perhaps a year.

18 **What did these men tell the church when they arrived back at Antioch of Syria?**

19 **What "door" did Paul say had been opened?** (See v. 27.)

20 Paul and Barnabas gave a "good report" to their "sending church" at Antioch of Syria. **Give examples of how missionaries have done that in your church.**

Key Verse

Nevertheless He did not leave Himself without witness, in that He did good, gave us rain from heaven and fruitful seasons, filling our hearts with food and gladness.

Acts 14:17

What's It Mean?

bygone—Past (v. 16).
commended—Given over to, or entrusted to (vv. 23 and 26).
exhorting—Encouraging strongly (v. 22).

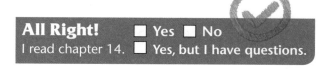

All Right!   ☐ Yes ☐ No
I read chapter 14.   ☐ Yes, but I have questions.

| Date: A.D. 48–49 | Place: Antioch, Jerusalem | Roman Emperor: Claudius | Local Ruler: Procurator |

1 **What city of Judea do you think** "certain men" **of verse 1 came from?** (See chp. 11.)

_____

2 **What** problem **had arisen, according to verses 1–2?**

"So the apostles and elders came together to consider this matter" (Acts 15:6).

This gathering, commonly called the council of Jerusalem, took place in A.D. 49.

3 **How** did the brothers of Phoenicia and Samaria feel **about the Gentiles** receiving **salvation?**

_____

4 **When these men got to Jerusalem, what did they** report? (See v. 4b.)

8 Find **the phrase** "a good while ago" **in verse 7.** Complete **the steps below to determine** how long ago **this was:**

Date of the council of Jerusalem. A.D. _____ minus the approximate date of Peter's first encounter with the salvation of Gentiles (chapter 10). A.D. _____ = **how long?** _____

5 **Why does it** not surprise **you that the Pharisees required** strict **adherence to the Jewish law for salvation?** (*Refer back to chapter 4 of the workbook.*)

9 **What important** verses **in Acts 10 come to your mind when you read verses 8–9 of Acts 15?** Write **them out.**

6 **Was the meeting of verses 6–7** pleasant? **To answer,** add a smile or a frown **to the face.**

7 **Who was one of the Gentiles Peter referred to in verse 7b?** (*You met him in Acts 10.*)

_____

10 **How is everyone's heart** purified?

_____

11 **How were some of these Jews** testing **God** (verse 10)**?**

What "yoke" **is mentioned here?** (Read verses 1 and 5.)

What is a literal **yoke, and** why **do you think Peter uses this particular figure of speech?**

12 **According to Peter, can any** physical act **save us?** ☐ Yes ☐ No Write **out the verse that supports your answer, including the** reference.

13 **What is the** surname **of this Simon mentioned in verse 14?** (Read Matthew 4:18.)

14 **What was the** point **of James' speech?** (See verse 19.)

15 **What did James use to** prove **his point?** (Read verses 15–17 and fill in the letters to solve the puzzle.)

__ c __ __ p t __ __ e

16 **On a separate sheet of paper, write in your** own words **the letter sent to the Gentile believers of Antioch.**

Four Requirements

Verse 20 tells four things the Gentiles were to abstain from:
1. Things offered to idols
2. Things strangled (meat that had the blood left in it because the animal was strangled rather than its throat cut)
3. Blood
4. Sexual immorality

Though not required for salvation, these things were important for a Christian's walk and witness in Antioch. *The first three were vital for the Gentiles' witness to the large Jewish population* of the city. Note that the first three prohibited acts were repulsive to the Jews. *The fourth is still essential for the purity not just of converted Jews but of all Christians.*

17 The crossword puzzle is made up of words used at the council of Jerusalem. **Use Acts 15:22–28 and the clues below to help you complete it.**

Across

  2 Directed the writing of the letter to Antioch

  5 Went with Paul and Barnabas to Antioch

  6 The council's feelings toward Barnabas and Paul, as revealed in the letter

Down

  1 The council was "assembled with one ___ ," or in agreement

  3 Went with Paul and Barnabas to Antioch

  4 Barnabas and Paul "___ their lives for the name of our Lord Jesus Christ"

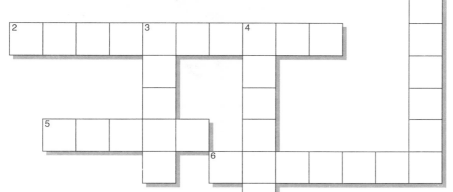

18 **Note in verse 24 that some went out without authorization. Could a system of accountability have stopped this?**
☐ Yes ☐ No **Explain your answer.**

19 **What was the response of the people of Antioch when they received the letter?**
Unscramble the letters. They c r e j i d o e =
They _____.

20 Barnabas and Paul took a letter to the Gentiles with the results of the council's decision. **Who was sent to tell them by word of mouth?**
_____

21 **What do you think were two primary jobs of the prophet in the early church? Fill in the letters.**
They e_____ and s_____ the _____.

After Some Days

The "after some days" of verse 36 is approximately one year after the Jerusalem Council.

22 **Who remained in Antioch?**

23 **What did Paul and Barnabas do while in Antioch?**

24 At the end of chapter 15, we see that Paul and Barnabas do not agree on whether John Mark should accompany them on the next missionary journey. **List reasons why you think each man responded as he did.**

Why Paul rejected Mark:

Why Barnabas wanted Mark:

25 **On a scale of 1 to 5, where 1 = mild and 5 = sharp, rate the level of the disagreement between Paul and Barnabas. (Circle one.) What two words in verse 39 tell you that?**
1 2 3 4 5; _____ and _____

26 How **was the disagreement** resolved?

DIGGING   DEEPER

28 **Read the following verses and tell what Paul's later attitude is toward Barnabas and Mark.**
1 Corinthians 9:6

2 Timothy 4:11

29 **In your opinion who was right? Explain your answer.**

27 **Fill in the blanks to show the two new** teams **and** where **they went.**

_____ and _____ went to Cyprus.

_____ and _____ went to Syria and Cilicia.

30 **Do good Christians have disagreements?**
Explain your answer. ☐ Yes ☐ No

What's It Mean?

abstain—Not to do something; to refrain from doing something, often as an act of self-denial (vv. 20 and 29).

accountability—Condition of being answerable to someone else; state of being responsible to someone for doing something (question 18).

adherence—Consistent support and loyalty (question 5).

dissension—Disagreement (v. 2).

procurator—In the context of Acts, a procurator was a Roman officer, entrusted with financial affairs of a province, often having administrative powers. Procurators often ruled Palestine during the New Testament period. Those mentioned in the Scriptures are Pilate, from A.D. 26–36; Felix, from 52–58; and Festus, from 58–62.

yoke—Literally, a wooden bar or frame for joining two draft animals (as oxen) for working together; used figuratively, a yoke is a burden (v. 10).

MEDITATION

This chapter is full of important information for God's people and His church. Prayerfully think over this information and write a paragraph on what God has revealed to you in His Word.

Key Verse   *But we believe that through the grace of the Lord Jesus Christ we shall be saved in the same manner as they.*   Acts 15:11

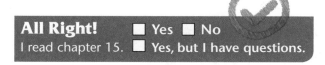

All Right!   ☐ Yes ☐ No
I read chapter 15.   ☐ Yes, but I have questions.

· IN A PHILIPPIAN JAIL ·

MISSIONARY JOURNEY TWO

| Date: A.D. 50 | Place: Antioch, Philippi | Roman Emperor: Claudius | Local Ruler: Herod Agrippa II |

1 **List some things we learn here about Timothy.**

1. He lived in _____ or _____.

2. His mother was a _____ woman who _____.

3. His father was _____.

4. He was _____ by the brethren (Christians) who lived in Lystra and Iconium.

Read 2 Timothy 1:5 before completing 5 and 6.

5. His mother was _____ and his grand-mother was _____.

6. Both of these women, and Timothy himself, had genuine _____.

2 Read 1 Timothy 4:12. In 1 Timothy Paul addressed Timothy some fifteen years after the time of Acts 16. **What age group do you think Timothy was in chapter 16? (Circle one.)**

teens

twenties

thirties

forties

fifties

3 Verse 4 says, "And as they went through the cities, they delivered to them the decrees to keep, which were determined by the apostles and elders at Jerusalem." **What decrees would these have been?** (See chapter 15.)

4 In the Jerusalem Council, Paul had strongly opposed requiring Christians to be circumcised (chapter 15). **Why then do we read in the very next chapter that he had Timothy circumcised?**

5 **What was the result of their traveling from town to town (Acts 16:5)?**

6 **Paul and his companions wanted to preach in Asia (verse 7), but God prevented them from doing so. Why?**

7 **Write portions of two verses in this chapter showing that Paul and his companions were sensitive to the Holy Spirit's leading.**

DIGGING DEEPER

8 Verse 7 says, "The Spirit did not permit them." Many Bible scholars believe this is referring to the Spirit of Jesus. Carefully read verses 6–7 and Acts 5:3–4 and 9. **According to these verses, what is the relationship between the Holy Spirit, the Spirit of Jesus, and the Spirit of God?**

9 **What was the message of Paul's vision from Macedonia (Acts 16:9b)?**

10 **At Troas a new companion was added to Paul's mission trip. Who was it?** (Read v. 10 carefully.)

11 **According to verse 14, who was Lydia?**

"Seller of purple"

Purple was purple cloth made in Thyatira that was noted for the quality of its purple dye.

Complete the words below that describe Lydia's personality.

PER _ _ _ SIVE

HOS _ _ _ ABLE

Roman Colony

It was a great privilege to belong to a Roman colony. Colonies elected their own officials and did not have to pay taxes to Rome. To maintain their colony status, they had to show loyalty to Rome, honor Roman law, and maintain civil control.

Philippi **5** facts:

1. It was named after Philip of Macedon, father of Alexander the Great.
2. It was a major city of the region of Macedonia.
3. Many retired Roman soldiers lived there.
4. It enjoyed the privileges of a Roman colony.
5. It had a very small population of Jews and no synagogue.

12 **Why did Lydia respond to Paul's message?**

How does this relate to Luke 24:45?

How should we relate this to our own efforts to witness?

13 Solve the **cryptogram** below, which tells a truth about **Paul and his companions.** Read the instructions in chapter 8 on how to solve cryptograms. The answer is a statement about Paul and his friends. Knowing about the events in chapter 16 will help you find the answers.

D	Y	U	N	U		I	U	O		V	M	U

D	Y	U		N	U	M	S	V	O	D	N		A	X

D	Y	U		I	A	N	D		Y	F	Q	Y		Q	A	C

B	Y	A		T	M	A	W	Z	V	F	I

D	A		H	N		D	Y	U		B	V	L		A	X

N	V	Z	S	V	D	F	A	O

14 **Why** were Paul and Silas thrown into prison at Philippi?

15 Verse 25 says, "But at midnight Paul and Silas were praying and singing hymns to God." **If you were there, what** three **songs** would you sing?

What words **would be in your prayer?** (Write your prayer in the back of your workbook.)

16 **Why did the jailer want to** kill himself?

17 **Have you** ever asked **(perhaps in a different way) the question that the jailor asked in verse 30?** "Sirs, what must I do to be saved?" ☐Yes ☐No **If you said yes,** briefly describe **this event.**

18 **Write out an** 11-word **statement on how to be saved that comes directly from Acts 16.**

19 **Who was** saved **in the jail?**

What caused him to seek the Lord?

20 Look back at Acts chapter 8. What word in verse 33 strongly indicates the importance of baptism to believers? (Read the note about "Baptism" on page 38 of your workbook.)

_____

21 What did the jailer do that indicates his feelings about his belief in God?

_____

Roman Citizenship

Roman citizenship carried many privileges, including the right to vote, the right to a proper trial, and exclusion from degrading forms of punishment, such as beating and crucifixion. Citizens carried certificates made of wood or metal that bore the names of witnesses to their citizenship.

Roman citizenship could be received

1. as a reward (perhaps for some heroic action or show of loyalty to Rome)

2. by paying a large sum of money (sometimes as a bribe)

3. by being born a Roman citizen (more significant than the above two)

Paul was born a Roman citizen (Acts 22:28).

22 Considering the information on Roman colonies and Roman citizenship, why would the magistrates be afraid as mentioned in verse 38?

23 Is Paul crazy? In verse 23 Paul says nothing about his Roman citizenship, which would have prevented his beating and his time in jail. After all this, in verse 37 he declares his Roman citizenship and demands their humiliation. Explain his actions.

24 What did Paul and Silas do for the brethren before they departed?

_____

What's It Mean?

decree—A decision by an individual or council (v. 4).
spirit of divination—Demonic spirit (v. 16).
magistrates—Local rulers (vv. 22, 35, 36, and 38).

Key Verse

Believe on the Lord Jesus Christ, and you will be saved.

Acts 16:31

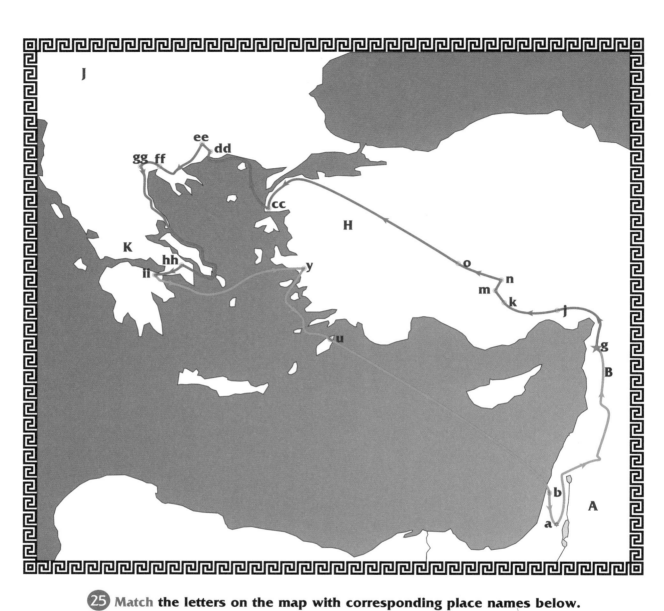

25 **Match the letters on the map with corresponding place names below.**

CITIES

____ Antioch	____ Lystra
____ Athens	____ Neapolis
____ Berea	____ Philippi
____ Caesarea	____ Pisidian Antioch
____ Corinth	____ Rhodes
____ Derbe	____ Tarsus
____ Ephesus	____ Thessalonica
____ Iconium	____ Troas
____ Jerusalem	

REGIONS

____ Achaia	____ Macedonia
____ Asia	____ Palestine
____ Galatia	____ Syria

All Right!
I read chapter 16.
☐ Yes ☐ No
☐ Yes, but I have questions.

Date: A.D. 51	Place: Philippi, Thessalonica, Berea, Athens	Roman Emperor: Claudius	Local Ruler: Herod Agrippa II

1 **What companion of Paul is not with him now?** Perhaps he stayed in Philippi. (Notice the word *they* in v. 1.)

_____

2 **List three verbs—one *-ed* word and two *-ing* words—that tell how Paul evangelized the Jews who were in the synagogue.**

1. _____

2. _____

3. _____

3 **What were the Jews envious of in verse 5?**

What did they do?

Thessalonica **5** **facts:**

1. It was the capital of Macedonia.
2. It had a synagogue.
3. It was a major seaport and trade center.
4. It was a free city, not governed by Rome.
5. Its population was over 200,000.

4 **What decree of Caesar were Paul and his companions accused of defying?**

5 **Compare the character of the Bereans with that of the Thessalonians.**

6 **Did the Bereans just accept Paul's message without question?**
☐ Yes ☐ No **Write the verse that tells what they did with what Paul said:**

LET'S BE BEREANS!

How should we apply the wisdom of the Bereans to our lives?

"Not a few" means *"many."*

The *"leading women"* of Thessalonica were women with influence in the affairs of the city; similar to the *"prominent women"* of Berea mentioned in verse 12.

7 **What happened that caused Paul to leave Berea** (Acts 17:13)**?**

8 **Who was Paul waiting for in Athens?**
S_____ and T_____

9 In verse 16 "his spirit was provoked" (NKJV) means he was "greatly distressed" (NIV). **Why was Paul greatly distressed?**

10 **Should we be greatly distressed today?**
☐ Yes ☐ No **Why?**

11 **According to verse 17, who was able to hear Paul's message?**

12 **Why did the philosophers say that Paul was promoting foreign gods?**

Prevailing Greek Philosophies

During Paul's time, **Epicureanism** taught that sensual and material pleasure was the greatest good.

Stoicism taught that individuals should be self-dependent and that sensual and material pleasure was to be suppressed.

Areopagus (Mars Hill)
In New Testament times the Areopagus, located at the northwest base of the Acropolis, was a 377-foot-high meeting place where people met for philosophical and religious debate and lectures.

13 **Where did Paul preach according to verse 19?**

Athens 5 facts:

1. It was the capital of Achaia and is also the capital of modern Greece.

2. It was the cultural and religious center of Greece.

3. It was named after the patron goddess Athena, the Greek goddess of wisdom (Minerva to the Romans).

4. Overlooking the city was the Acropolis, a 500-foot-high hill topped with several temples, including the magnificent Parthenon.

5. It was a university city noted for its many pagan philosophers.

14 **Using verse 21, describe in your own words the Athenians at the Areopagus.**

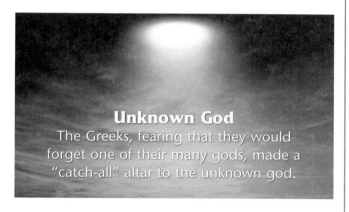

Unknown God
The Greeks, fearing that they would forget one of their many gods, made a "catch-all" altar to the unknown god.

15 **Who is the One that Paul is proclaiming to the Athenians?**

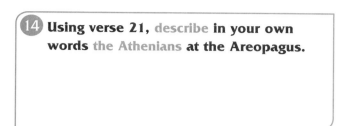

DIGGING DEEPER

17 Read Acts 17:25 and the two verses below. "For since the beginning of the world men have not heard nor perceived by the ear, nor has the eye seen any God besides You, who acts for the one who waits for Him" (Isaiah 64:4).

"For even the Son of Man did not come to be served, but to serve, and to give His life a ransom for many" (Mark 10:45).

Does God need anything from us? ☐ Yes ☐ No
Do we need anything from God? ☐ Yes ☐ No
Write what God does for us:

Acts 17:25

Isaiah 64:4

Mark 10:45

Across

2 Jesus was ___ from the dead.
7 God has ___ each person's preappointed times.
8 Paul quoted from some Roman ___.
9 "In Him we live and move and have our ___."
10 The Athenians had an altar to one they called "the ___ god."
11 Paul's God is not worshiped with our ___.

16 This crossword is made up of ideas from Paul's great sermon to the Athenians. **Use the clues above and verses 22–31 to help you solve the puzzle.**

Down

1 "He gives to all ___, breath, and all things."
2 Paul said that the Athenians were very ___.
3 Paul said that God would ___ the world.
4 "[God] is not ___ from each one of us."
5 God wants us to ___ Him.
6 God commands men everywhere to ___.

75

18 **Explain** why verse 26 should be important to you?

19 **What were** the two **responses to Paul's gospel message?**

1.

2.

20 **Circle** the words that best describe **Paul's message to the people of Athens.**

eloquent   weak   wise

fearful   trembling   persuasive

21 **Did** many **people respond to Paul's message in Athens?** ☐ Yes ☐ No

Name two **who responded.**

_____

_____

Areopagite

A member of the Areopagus court, which judged the things said at the Areopagus. At one time it was a criminal court, but in Paul's day it judged religious and philosophical matters.

"Your own poets"

Paul did not limit his study to the Bible and Jewish literature. He was very knowledgeable of Greek literature and culture. In Acts 17:28 he quotes two well-known Greek poets. The phrase *"For in Him we live and move and have our being"* came from the Cicilian poet **Aratus** (a Stoic). The phrase *"For we are also His offspring"* was penned by the Cretan poet **Epimenides**, who is again quoted by Paul in Titus 1:12: *"Cretans are always liars, evil beasts, lazy gluttons."* In 1 Corinthians 15:33 Paul quotes an Athenian comic poet named **Menander**: *"Evil company corrupts good habits."* ("Bad company corrupts good character," NIV.)

What's It Mean?

conducted—Guided or directed (v. 15).
preappointed—Appointed ahead of time (v. 26).
security—A sum of money given to assure a person's appearance in court. (v. 9)

Key Verse

Nor is He worshiped with men's hands, as though He needed anything, since He gives to all life, breath, and all things.

Acts 17:25

All Right! ■ Yes ■ No
I read chapter 17. ■ Yes, but I have questions.

| Date: A.D. 51–52 | Place: Ephesus, Corinth | Roman Emperor: Claudius | Local Ruler: Herod Agrippa II |

1 **Where did Paul go from Athens?**

_____

2 **Who was the Roman emperor at this time?**
(See v. 2.) _____

5

Corinth 5 **facts:**

1. It was a major east-west trade center and one of the most important commercial cities of the empire.

2. It had a synagogue.

3. It was the home of the temple of Aphrodite, the Greek goddess of love (the Roman goddess Venus).

4. It was known for its materialism and open immorality.

5. Its population was over 250,000 free people, as well as many slaves.

3 **Whom did Paul meet in Corinth?** (See v. 2.)

What did Paul have in common with this couple?

4 **Write the verse that tells what Paul did in the synagogue of Corinth.**

DIGGING DEEPER

5 In 1 Corinthians 2:2–5 Paul describes how he preached in Corinth. **Read these verses, and circle the words that describe his preaching in Corinth.**

eloquent   weak   wise
fearful   trembling   persuasive

Describe the difference between Paul's preaching in Corinth and in Athens.
(See question 20 in chapter 17.)

Explain why there is this difference.

SOLVE THE MYSTERY

6 While Paul was in Corinth, he wrote two letters to one of the cities in Macedonia. **What two books of the Bible did those letters become?**

_____

7 **What do we learn about the man called Crispus?**

8 **List five encouraging things that the Lord said to Paul.** (See vv. 9 and 10.)

1. _____
2. _____
3. _____
4. _____
5. _____

9 **Why could the Lord's words in verse 10 be called Paul's life assurance policy?**

10 **How many months did Paul stay in Corinth teaching the Word?**

_____

Gallio

As noted in verse 12, Gallio was the proconsul of Achaia. (Achaia and Macedonia made up ancient Greece.) He was well liked by the people of that region, known to be even-tempered and fair. An inscription places him in Achaia in A.D. 51–52, enabling historians to date Paul's visit to Corinth.

11 **What happened to Sosthenes?**

_____

12 **Where and why did Paul have his hair cut off?**

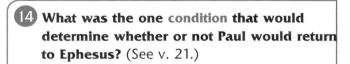

Ephesus 5 facts:

1. It was the capital, largest, and most famous city of Asia Minor during Paul's time.
2. It was a major commercial crossroad.
3. It was the home of the temple of the Greek goddess Artemis (the Roman goddess Diana), which no longer exists but is considered one of the "seven wonders of the ancient world."
4. It had a magnificent theater that could seat 25,000 people.
5. Its population was believed to be around 250,000.

13 **Why did Paul not stay longer when the Jews wanted him to?**

14 **What was the one condition that would determine whether or not Paul would return to Ephesus?** (See v. 21.)

How often do you say "if it is God's will"?

15 What in verse 22 tells us that it was the Jerusalem church that Paul greeted?

16 What churches is Paul likely to have visited in Galatia and Phrygia? (Complete the city names.)

D_____

L_____

I_____

P_____ A_____

Paul's Third Missionary Journey

In verses 22 and 23 the reader suddenly finds Paul arriving in Palestine and then in Galatia on a new missionary journey. The estimated dates for this third journey are A.D. 53–57.

17 In verse 24 the story returns to Ephesus, telling the reader about a man named Apollos. **Complete the crisscross puzzle with words that tell about Apollos.** Solve the puzzle by placing the missing words from verses 24 and 25 below into the correct row or column.

Now a certain ___ named Apollos, born at Alexandria, an ___ man and ___ in the Scriptures, came to Ephesus. This man had been ___ in the way of the Lord; and being ___ in spirit, he spoke and ___ accurately the things of the Lord, though he knew only the baptism of ___ (Acts 18:24–25).

18 What did Aquila and Priscilla do for Apollos?

19 What city of Achaia do you think Apollos went to? (Look at the map in chapter 16.)

_____

20 What great gift, or ability, did Apollos have? (Read verse 29.)

_____

What's the Difference?

Baptism of John: a baptism of repentance.

Baptism of Jesus: a picture of faith in the finished work of Christ.

ALEXANDRIA

Key Verses

Now the Lord spoke to Paul in the night by a vision, "Do not be afraid, but speak, and do not keep silent; for I am with you, and no one will attack you to hurt you; for I have many people in this city."

Acts 18:9–10

What's It Mean?

compelled—Moved to action often by a powerful inner force (v. 5).
eloquent—Able to speak and express oneself with clarity and power (v. 24).
fervent—Passionate; marked by intensity of feeling (v. 25).

· APOLLOS DEBATING ·

All Right!   ☐ Yes ☐ No
I read chapter 18. ☐ Yes, but I have questions.

MISSIONARY JOURNEY THREE

| Date: A.D. 53–55 | Place: Ephesus | Roman Emperor: Claudius/Nero | Local Ruler: Herod Agrippa II |

1 **What did Paul discover about the disciples at Ephesus?** (See vv. 1–7.)

Who had made these men disciples?

Do you think they were saved before they met Paul? ☐ Yes ☐ No **Explain your answer.**

School of Tyrannus
Paul may have worked from daylight until 11:00 A.M. and spent the afternoons teaching in the lecture hall of Tyrannus, which would have been available to him after 11:00 A.M., since that's when public life ended.

2 **Circle four words that tell about Paul's ministry in the synagogue at Ephesus.**

six months   persuading   meek

reasoning   boldly   three months

3 **In verse 9 Christians are called** "the Way." **What verse in John 14 gives a reason for this title?** JOHN 14:___

4 **How long did Paul teach in Ephesus?** Verse 10 says _____ years, but in Acts 20:31, when Paul is speaking to the Ephesian elders, he says _____ years. Perhaps in chapter 20 he is talking about his total number of years in Ephesus. **According to verse 10, what were the results?**

5 **What one word describes the miracles God worked through Paul?** (See v. 11.) Complete **the word.**
u n __ __ __ __ __

6 **Why did the man possessed by evil spirits attack the seven sons of the Jewish priest named Sceva?**

7 **What was the result of this event? Fill in the words from vv. 17 and 20.**
_____ fell on them all [the Jews and Greeks in Ephesus], and the _____ of the Lord Jesus was magnified.

So the word of the Lord _____ mightily and prevailed.

8 **What did the** Spirit tell Paul **in verse 21?**

9 Paul planned to visit Macedonia and Achaia before going to Rome. **What are** four cities **we can be fairly sure he visited?**

1._____   3._____

2._____   4._____

SOLVE THE MYSTERY

10 Complete **the sentences with the** names **of four of Paul's traveling companions:**

_____ and _____

went on ahead to Macedonia. (See v. 22.)

_____ and _____

stayed with Paul in Ephesus. (See v. 29.)

DIGGING DEEPER

11 **Find out more about** Erastus **from 2 Timothy 4:20 and Romans 16:23.** Where **was Paul most likely to have met him?** _____
What was his job? _____

12 **Verse 26 tells what** Demetrius **said about Paul. Do you think what he said was** true?
☐ Yes ☐ No

LETTERS
WRITTEN
FROM EPHESUS:
1 Corinthians and perhaps Galatians

Diana

The Greek name of the goddess was Artemis, and her Roman name was Diana. At Ephesus she was considered the mother goddess of fertility, and that city was the caretaker of her temple.

13 **According to verse 31, who were the** friends of Paul **that pleaded with him to stay out of the theater?**

_____

14 Verse 29 tells us that the whole city rushed into the theater, yet in verse 32 most of the crowd did not even know why they were there. **What** word **in verse 29** best describes **the situation?** (A form of the word appears in v. 32.)

_____

Who were these people following?
(Circle one.)

Paul   Demetrius

The person in front of them

Have you been caught up **in something wrong when you had** not intended **to be?**
☐ Yes ☐ No Briefly **tell what happened:**

83

15 **Using the five boxes below, describe the sequence of events of the riot at Ephesus, using words or pictures.**

1

2

3

4

5

16 **Why did the riot end quietly?**

SOLVE THE ANALOGY

17 **Athena was to Athens as _____ was to Ephesus.**

18 **This crossword puzzle is made up of words that appear in Acts 19. Use the chapter and the clues below to help you solve the puzzle.**

Across

1 A Jewish chief priest who had seven sons.

5 This man was put in front of the crowd to speak.

6 This man was a silversmith who stirred up the riot at Ephesus.

Down

2 This man quieted and dismissed the crowd.

3 This man was head of a school in Ephesus.

4 This man, a Macedonian, was seized by the crowd.

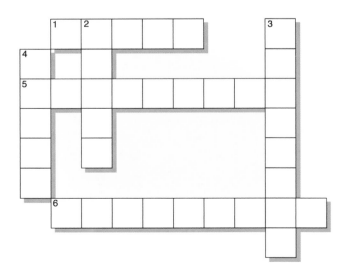

SOLVE THE MYSTERY

19 **Paul wrote a letter while in Ephesus. Follow the steps of logic below to determine which letter he wrote.**

1. Read 1 Corinthians 16:21.
   Who wrote this letter?

   _____

2. Read 1 Corinthians 16:7–8.
   Where was he when he wrote it?

   _____

3. Read 1 Corinthians 1:2.
   To whom was he writing?

   _____

4. **The letter Paul wrote from Ephesus** was

   _____.

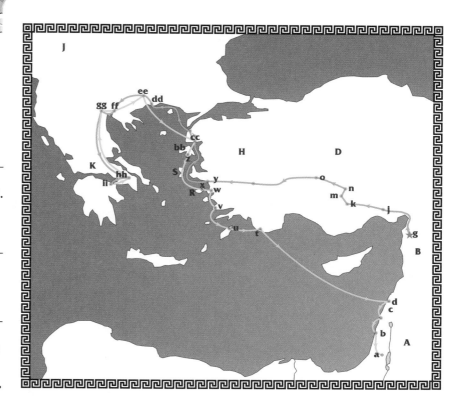

20 **Match the letters on the map with corresponding place names below.**

___ Achaia	___ Cyprus	___ Macedonia	___ Ptolemais
___ Antioch	___ Derbe	___ Miletus	___ Rhodes
___ Asia	___ Ephesus	___ Mitylene	___ Stamos
___ Assos	___ Galatia	___ Neapolis	___ Syria
___ Athens	___ Iconium	___ Palestine	___ Tarsus
___ Berea	___ Jerusalem	___ Patara	___ Thessalonica
___ Caesarea	___ Kios	___ Philippi	___ Troas
___ Cilicia	___ Kos	___ Pisidian Antioch	___ Trogyllium
___ Corinth	___ Lystra		___ Tyre

Key Verse

So the word of the Lord grew mightily and prevailed.

Acts 19:20

What's It Mean?

exorcise—To cast out demons (v. 13).

exorcists—People who cast out demons (v. 13).

itinerant—Traveling from place to place (v. 13).

prevailed—Became effective; predominated; triumphed (vv. 16 and 20).

purposed—In this context, "decided"; usually, the word *purpose* is a noun; less often, as here (v. 21), it is a verb, as in "I purpose to complete the assignment."

85

All Right!
I read chapter 19.
☐ Yes ☐ No
☐ Yes, but I have questions.

Date: A.D. 56–57	Place: Ephesus to Miletus	Roman Emperor: Nero	Local Ruler: Herod Agrippa II

1 **What did Paul do in the region of Macedonia?**

_____

_____

2 **What town in Greece do you think he stayed in for three months?**
(As named here, "Greece" consists largely of Achaia.)

_____

_____

3 **Was the door to sail to Syria open or shut?**
☐ Open ☐ Shut
What caused it to be that way?

What new door was opened to Paul?

_____

4 **In verses 5–6, who do we know stayed with Paul and then later sailed with him to Troas?**

_____

_____

5 **Why did Eutychus fall asleep?**

Can you relate? ☐ Yes ☐ No **Explain.**

6 **What was the result of this event?**
(Read v. 12.)

ANALOGY

7 **Paul is to Eutychus as Peter is to**

_____

8 Verse 13 tells us that Paul went down on foot from Troas to Assos. **Why do you think he walked instead of taking a ship?**

9 Verse 16 says that Paul passed Ephesus because he was in a hurry. **Why didn't he stop to say hello to his friends?**

What group from the Ephesian church did Paul meet in Miletus, and why?

What It Means
The term "not a little comforted" in verse 12 means comforted a lot, or greatly encouraged.

LETTER WRITTEN FROM CORINTH: Romans

10 List four **things Paul had done in his ministry at Ephesus as mentioned in verses 19–21.**

11 Why **did Paul insist on going back to Jerusalem when he did not know what would happen to him?** (See v. 22.)

12 What did Paul **know he would face in** every **city?** Circle **those that are correct:**

chains   kindness   helpfulness

smiles   tribulation   heartbreak

DIGGING   DEEPER

13 What was Paul's attitude **toward those things he knew he would face?** Write the verse **that tells you.**

Second Timothy is Paul's last letter; soon he will be executed. Read Acts 20:24 and compare it with some of his last words ten years later in 2 Timothy 4:6–7.

What is said in verse 24?

How was it fulfilled according to 2 Timothy?

Is your goal and desire the same as Paul's? ☐ Yes ☐ No In what way?

14 Read verses 26–27. How could we be guilty **of the blood of man?**

LETTER WRITTEN FROM PHILIPPI: 2 Corinthians

15 **Why does Paul say in verse 28 "Therefore take heed to yourselves" and in verse 31 "Therefore watch"?**

16 **Complete the phrases related to how Paul warns the elders of Ephesus:**
1. I did not c_____ to warn everyone
2. warned night and day with t_____

17 **Was Paul being paid to minister to the Ephesians?** ☐ Yes ☐ No **Give scriptural evidence for your answer from Acts 20.**

18 **What words of Jesus did Paul want the people in Miletus to remember?**

19 This word search contains words describing Paul's departure from Miletus as noted in Acts 20:36–37. **Circle five words found in, or related to, these verses.**

P	R	A	Y	E	D	S
K	D	W	E	P	T	H
T	S	E	O	F	U	A
L	L	Y	S	G	A	H
E	B	S	G	S	Q	N
N	B	E	E	P	I	G
K	D	Q	M	R	N	K

20 **Have any of your departures been similar to Paul's departure from Miletus?** ☐ Yes ☐ No **If yes, describe one.**

21 **What grieved the people most?**

What's It Mean?

heed—Watch out, pay careful attention (v. 28).
shunned—Deliberately avoided (v. 27: "I have not hesitated to proclaim . . ." in the NIV).
tribulations—Trials, difficulties, sufferings (v. 23).

Key Verse

But none of these things move me; nor do I count my life dear to myself, so that I may finish my race with joy, and the ministry which I received from the Lord Jesus, to testify to the gospel of the grace of God.

Acts 20:24

What It Means
The words *"fell on Paul's neck"* in v. 37 mean they embraced, or hugged.

All Right! ☐ Yes ☐ No
I read chapter 20. ☐ Yes, but I have questions.

TRIALS IN JERUSALEM AND CAESAREA

| Date: A.D. 57 | Place: Miletus to Jerusalem | Roman Emperor: Nero | Local Ruler: Herod Agrippa II, Felix (Procurator of Judea) |

1 **Circle the** destination **in Phoenicia where Paul and his companions** stayed **for seven days after leaving Miletus:**

Troas   Tyre   Tarsus

Ephesus   Thessalonica   Philippi

An Interesting Contrast

While Paul traveled to **many different places** all over the Roman Empire, Philip probably ministered in **select locations**, in and around one city—Caesarea.

2 Verse 4 says that through the Spirit the disciples of Tyre urged Paul not to go to Jerusalem, but in 20:22 Paul was "bound in the Spirit" to go to Jerusalem. **Is the Spirit** contradicting **Himself?** ☐ Yes ☐ No Explain **your answer.**

6 **What was the** setting **when we last read of Agabus? Where was he, and what did he** prophesy? (Read Acts 11:27–29.)

What is his warning **in chapter 21?**

A	N	E	P	A	O	W	N
K	N	D	L	T	R	D	Y	E	D

3 **Use the scrambled letters above the blank boxes to form a** four-word phrase **telling what Paul and the disciples did just before Paul left them at Tyre.**

4 **Who was** Philip?

What city **was Philip in when we last read about him?** (Read Acts 8:40.)

_____

Where **is he** now **in Acts 21?**

_____

SOLVE THE MYSTERY

7 **Who are the** "we" **of verse 12?** (Check out Acts 20.) The first letter of each name is given below.

S_____   T_____
A_____   G_____
S_____   T_____
T_____   L_____

8 **What were Paul's** feelings **about their pleading with him to not go to Jerusalem?**

What answer **did he give them?** (Write the relevant part of a verse.)

5 Note the dates for the events of chapter 8 and chapter 21. How long **had Philip apparently ministered in Caesarea?**

_____

9 All these people who were pleading with him to not go were very godly men. **Who was** right? ☐ Other disciples ☐ Paul Explain **your answer.**

10 **What seven-word** concession **did the disciples make?** (See v. 14.)

_____

11 **What** problem **arose again in Jerusalem among many Christians, as noted in verses 20–21?**

12 **Why did Paul** purify **himself?**

13 In verse 25 Paul spoke of a decision that had been made seven years earlier. **What** event **did this decision come from? Read Acts 15; then** unscramble **the words to find the answer.**

hte inculoc fo usmeJelar

_____

14 Verse 27 says, "Jews from Asia, seeing him (Paul) in the Temple, stirred up the whole crowd." **What** city in Asia **do you think these Jews were from?**

_____

15 Describe **the events of verses 27–40 in a sequence of** five steps. **You may use words or draw pictures.**

> 1
>
> 2
>
> 3
>
> 4
>
> 5

Commander of the Garrison

His name was Claudius Lysias (23:26). He was in charge of keeping order in the city.

17 **From this chapter, what two languages do we know Paul spoke?**

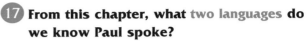

_____ and _____

16 Verse 31 tells us that "all Jerusalem was in an uproar," and in v. 34 "some among the multitude cried one thing and some another." **In what other city did we see a similar incident?** (Circle its name.)

Athens   Pisidian Antioch

Lystra   Corinth   Ephesus

Thessalonica   Philippi

The Barracks was the Fortress of Antonia, which was connected to the north end of the temple. The fortress had a tall tower overlooking the temple area. Thus any disturbance could easily be detected and troops immediately deployed.

MEDITATION

Carefully reflect on Paul's commitment to the moving of the Holy Spirit. Write a paragraph about how you can apply what you have learned to your own life.

What's It Mean?

concession—The act of conceding; acknowledgment or admission (item 10).
evangelist—A person who preaches the gospel, often traveling from place to place (v. 8).
uproar—A state of emotion, excitement, or violent disturbance (v. 31).
zealous—Committed to and excited about a cause (v. 20).

Key Verse

Then Paul answered, "What do you mean by weeping and breaking my heart? For I am ready not only to be bound, but also to die at Jerusalem for the name of the Lord Jesus."

Acts 21:13

92

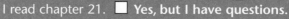

All Right!   ■ Yes ■ No
I read chapter 21.   ■ Yes, but I have questions.

| Date: A.D. 57 | Place: Jerusalem | Roman Emperor: Nero | Local Ruler: Herod Agrippa II, Felix (Procurator of Judea) |

1 **Complete seven facts about Paul before he was saved. He...**

1. was born in _____

2. was brought up in _____

3. was trained at the feet of _____

4. was taught according to the strictness of the Jewish _____

5. was _____ toward God

6. had persecuted Christians to _____

7. had believers bound and put in _____

List three more facts from Galatians 1:13–14. Paul...

8. _____ the church of God beyond measure

9. tried to _____ the church

10. was _____ in Judaism beyond others his own age

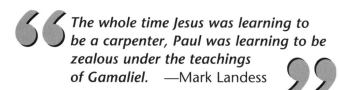

The whole time Jesus was learning to be a carpenter, Paul was learning to be zealous under the teachings of Gamaliel. —Mark Landess

2 **What group of people in the crowd had witnessed Saul as he persecuted Christians, or followers of the Way, to death and had seen him binding believers and delivering them to prison?** (Look back at the story of Stephen in chapters 6 and 7.)

4 God had told Ananias that Paul would see the Just One and hear His voice (verse 14). **Who is the Just One?**

_____

5 **Whom did Ananias say Paul would be a witness to?**

_____

SOLVE THE MYSTERY

6 **Read Acts 9:29–30.**

What new information can be added to the story in Acts 9 after hearing Paul's testimony in Acts 22? (Read Acts 22:17–21.)

"Threw dust into the air"
Perhaps an expression for throwing stones since they were prevented by the soldiers from stoning Paul.

"Tore off their clothes"
Threw off their outer garments as an expression of anger or frustration.

93

3 **Unscramble the following word from verse 10, which tells us that God had a plan for Paul:**   tanpipode = _____.

7 **What word caused Paul's audience to raise their voices against him?** (See vv. 21–22.)

_____

8 Below is a crisscross puzzle containing words that describe the Jews' response to Paul's speech. **Fill in the rows and columns of the puzzle with the missing words from verses 22–23:**

"And they listened to him until this word, and then they <u>RAISED</u> their voices and said, '___ with such a fellow from the earth, for he is not fit to ___!' Then, as they ___ out and ___ off their clothes and ___ dust into the air, . . ."

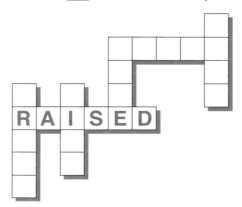

9 **What fact about Roman law is reinforced in verses 25–29?** (Check chapter 16.)

10 In chapter 16 Paul did not declare his Roman citizenship until after he was imprisoned. **Why do you think that Paul in verse 25 declared his Roman citizenship immediately?**

11 The Roman commander arranged for Paul to meet with some Jews the next day. Who were they?

"Examined under scourging"

The Romans were going to use torture to get information out of Paul. The scourge, or cat-o'-nine-tails, was a whip consisting of nine strands of leather with pieces of sharp metal, bone, or glass attached to each end. Each time the victim was struck, chunks of flesh were torn from the body. It was often used as an instrument for execution.

What's It Mean?

make haste—Hurry up (v. 18).
thongs—Strips, especially of leather or hide (v. 25).

Key Verse

Then [Ananias] said, "The God of our fathers has chosen you that you should know His will, and see the Just One, and hear the voice of His mouth."

Acts 22:14

All Right!   ☐ Yes ☐ No
I read chapter 22. ☐ Yes, but I have questions.

Date: A.D. 57	Place: Jerusalem to Caesarea	Roman Emperor: Nero	Local Ruler: Herod Agrippa II, Felix (Procurator of Judea)

1 **What words of Paul's caused him to receive a blow on the mouth?**

What did Paul say in response?

5 **Do you think the Sadducees and the Pharisees** got along **very well?** ☐ Yes ☐ No

6 **Why was the commander so** concerned **about Paul's safety?**

2 **What do you think he means by the words** "whitewashed wall"?

DIGGING DEEPER

3 **What** physical handicap **might Paul have had, as suggested in verse 5?** Galatians 4:15 and 6:11 hint at the same problem.

4 **What did Paul say to** confuse **the prosecutors?** Be sure to consider verses 6–9 before you answer. You also may need to review chapter 4 of your workbook.

7 **What verse in chapter 23 is** like Acts 18:9–10, **and** how **are these verses alike?**

Why could this passage also be called a term ("for a time") **life** assurance policy?

Do we, as believers, have a similar promise **today? Before you answer this question,** read Matthew 28:19–20 and Hebrews 13:5–6 and write the relevant words. ☐ Yes ☐ No

8 Solve the cryptogram below to determine what statement is common to Acts 18:9 and 27:23–24.

S	N	C		Y	Q	H	H	X		V	L	Z	H

U	N	Y		Y	N		G	Q		L	A	M	L	O	C

9 According to verse 11, where will Paul witness other than Jerusalem? (Circle the city.)

Corinth   Ephesus   Thessalonica

Philippi   Rome   Antioch

10 What did Paul's enemies plan to do to him?

11 How did God enable Paul to thwart his enemies' plans?

12 Circle how many military men (soldiers, horsemen, spearmen) escorted Paul out of Jerusalem:

10

100

230

270

470

Why Such an Escort? The Palestine countryside was very dangerous for Roman activity. The cruel and foolish governorship of Felix spurred the Jewish zealots into many covert operations. Apparently, Paul and his escort of Romans made it through the rugged Judean hills. With the risk of ambush lessened, only 70 horsemen accompanied Paul the rest of the way to Caesarea (v. 32).

⑬ **To whom was Paul sent next?**
(Circle the letters of his name.)

A Z F O G E T L I M S P X N

⑭ **Who wrote the letter to Felix?**

_____

**How many times is the personal pronoun
"I" used in the letter from the commander
to Felix?** (Read vv. 26–30.) _____
**Do you think the commander is trying to
get credit for the rescue?** ☐ Yes ☐ No

⑮ **What town in Cilicia did Paul come from?**

_____

⑯ **What do you think might have happened
to those who plotted to kill Paul?**

Herod's Praetorium

The Praetorium was originally the grand palace of King Herod the Great. Apparently, in Paul's day, the region's procurator lived in it.

Key Verse | **Acts 23:11**

But the following night the Lord stood by him and said, "Be of good cheer, Paul; for as you have testified for Me in Jerusalem, so you must also bear witness at Rome."

What's It Mean?

conspiracy—A secret plan against a person (v. 13).
revile—To abuse someone verbally (v. 4).
thwart—To prevent or stop something from happening.
  Zealot—Member of a fanatical sect arising in Judea during the first century A.D. and militantly opposing the Roman domination of Palestine.

All Right!
I read chapter 23. ☐ Yes ☐ No
☐ Yes, but I have questions.

Date: A.D. 57–59	Place: Caesarea	Roman Emperor: Nero	Local Ruler: Herod Agrippa II, Felix (Procurator of Judea)

1 Below are five steps describing Paul's court case before Governor Felix and its aftermath. In chapter 24, find the verse or verses that describe each step, and write the verse number(s) on the line.
(The first step is given.)

1. The Jews present their case. _____

2. Paul presents his case. _____

3. Felix adjourns the proceedings. _____

4. Felix orders the centurion to keep Paul under guard. _____

5. Paul witnesses to Felix and his wife about faith in Christ. _____

2 Below are scrambled words from verses 14–16, in which Paul confesses his faith before Felix. Read the verses; then unscramble each word and write it on the line.

hwrsoip: _____
Paul said, "I ___ the God of my fathers."

Lwa: _____
Paul believed everything written in the ___.

pehsortp: _____
He also believed everything written in the ___.

hepo: _____
Paul said, "I have ___ in God."

rinrsecurteo: _____
Paul said there would be a ___ of the dead.

icsnceecno: _____
Paul tried to have a ___ that did not offend God or men.

3 Should we confess the things Paul confessed to in verses 14–16? ☐ Yes ☐ No

4 For what reason does Paul feel he is being judged? (See v. 21.)

5 Who is Lysias, mentioned in verse 22? (Read Acts 23:26.)

Tiberius Claudius **Felix** was a *freedman* (once a slave and now free) who managed to rise to the position of *procurator* (governor) of Judea. The coarseness of his slave life carried over into his governorship, and he was noted for his lurid and cruel reign. He lost all patronage from the Jews and was eventually recalled to Rome by Nero.

Drusilla married her first husband, Azizus of Emesa, at age sixteen. After only one year of marriage to Azizus, Drusilla was courted by Felix and became his third wife.

Sect of the Nazarenes
Jews' term for Christianity

Tertullus
The lawyer for the Jews

6 **What kind of guard does Felix put Paul under?**

9 Verse 26 says that Felix was hoping Paul would give him money so Felix could release him. **In other words, Felix was hoping to be offered a _____.**
r e b b i (Unscramble the word.)

10 **Why does Felix think Paul has money?** (See v. 17.)

SOLVE THE MYSTERY

7 Verse 23 says that Felix lets friends visit Paul while he is under arrest. **Considering that Paul is in Caesarea, who might these friends be?** (Read Acts 21:8–11.)

11 **How long does Felix leave Paul in prison at Caesarea?** _____ Why?

What's It Mean?

adjourned—Suspended or closed indefinitely or until a later time (as a session or meeting).
profane—As a verb, to treat (something sacred) with irreverence or contempt (v. 6).
tedious—Difficult and boring; tiresome because of length or dullness (v. 4).

8 Paul talked personally to Felix (v. 25) about spiritual matters. **Complete the words below to tell what he talked about:**
R_____
S_____
J_____ to come
What was Felix's response?

Why do you think Paul's words made Felix uncomfortable?

Key Verse

I have hope in God, which they themselves also accept, that there will be a resurrection of the dead, both of the just and the unjust.

Acts 24:15

All Right!   ☐ Yes ☐ No
I read chapter 24. ☐ Yes, but I have questions.

| Date: A.D. 59 | Place: Caesarea | Roman Emperor: Nero | Local Ruler: Herod Agrippa II, Felix (Procurator of Judea) |

1 **What group of people that you previously read about are probably the ones who plan to ambush Paul in verse 3?**

3 **Could the Jews prove any of their charges?**
☐ Yes ☐ No

4 **Why did Festus want to send Paul to Jerusalem?**

2 **Before whom does Paul appear at the beginning of this chapter?**

_____

5 **Circle below who Paul thought should judge him.**

Festus   Jews   Caesar

Porcius **Festus** was governor of Judea for only two years. He was noted for his honesty and wisdom.

6 **Give the two possible reasons why Paul appealed to Caesar.**
1. (Read v. 9.)

2. (Read 23:11.)

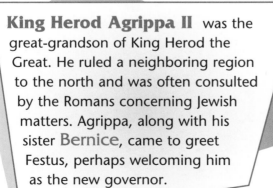

King Herod Agrippa II was the great-grandson of King Herod the Great. He ruled a neighboring region to the north and was often consulted by the Romans concerning Jewish matters. Agrippa, along with his sister **Bernice**, came to greet Festus, perhaps welcoming him as the new governor.

Appealing to Caesar

As a Roman citizen, Paul had the right to be tried before the Roman emperor or his representative.

7 **Complete the word search below by circling ten words that Paul used in his speech prior to his appeal to Caesar. Write the same words to fill in the blanks and complete verses 10–11:**

"So Paul said, 'I stand at Caesar's judgment seat, where I ought to be _____. To the Jews I have done no _____, as you very well know. For if I am an _____, or have _____ anything deserving of _____, I do not _____ to _____; but if there is _____ in these things of which these men _____ me, no one can _____ me to them. I appeal to Caesar.' "

D	C	A	C	C	U	S	E	P	E
N	E	O	J	U	D	G	E	D	O
O	O	A	M	K	G	Z	U	F	W
T	B	N	T	M	O	B	F	T	R
H	J	G	G	H	I	E	T	R	O
I	E	L	P	D	N	T	U	H	N
N	C	J	Y	D	M	Z	T	F	G
G	T	I	E	Q	Z	U	P	E	X
U	N	R	K	F	O	I	G	E	D
G	D	E	L	I	V	E	R	V	M

8 **Was Paul using his rights as a Roman citizen?** ☐ Yes ☐ No **Was his appeal mainly for himself or the kingdom of God?**

_____

9 **What was Festus' reply to Paul's appeal to Caesar?**

10 Verse 19 shows that Festus and Paul thought of Jesus in opposite ways. Write **one word in each space telling how they thought of Him.**

Festus thought Jesus was _____, but Paul knew He was _____.

11 **What was Festus' dilemma?** (See vv. 24–27.)

What's It Mean?

dilemma—A situation involving a difficult choice, in which one is uncertain what to do (question 11).
pomp—Fanfare or showiness (v. 23).

Key Verse

For if I am an offender, or have committed anything deserving of death, I do not object to dying; but if there is nothing in these things of which these men accuse me, no one can deliver me to them. I appeal to Caesar.

Acts 25:11

All Right! ☐ Yes ☐ No
I read chapter 25. ☐ Yes, but I have questions.

| Date: A.D. 59 | Place: Caesarea | Roman Emperor: Nero | Local Ruler: Herod Agrippa II, Felix (Procurator of Judea) |

1 **Whom** does Paul appear before in this chapter?

_____

"Expert in all customs"

King Agrippa was often consulted by the Romans concerning Jewish matters. Paul feels fortunate to present his case to him and acknowledges Agrippa's expertise in this area (v. 3).

2 Verse 4 reveals one more fact about Paul's training in Jerusalem. **What** is this fact?

3 **What** is the promise mentioned in verses **6–7?** (Read v. 8.)

4 **Why** do you think Paul asked the question in verse 8?

5 **In verse 19 Paul tells King Agrippa II that he was not disobedient to the vision from God. What was Paul obedient to?** Read verses 16–18, and fill in the missing words in the following paragraph:

Paul _____ and _____ to the things he had seen and the things God had revealed to him. He showed the _____ people as well as the _____ how to turn from _____ to _____ so that they would receive _____ of sins and an _____ among those who are sanctified by _____ in Christ.

Are you obedient to what God has shown you in His Word? ☐ Yes ☐ No

If you answered yes, prove your answer by giving three recent examples of your obedience to Christ:

1.

2.

3.

6 **What is the natural result of repenting and turning toward God?** (Read v. 20 and note the information box.)
Complete **the phrase below.**

Good _____

> ### "Do works befitting repentance"
> (v. 20) Below are three translations:
> 1. "prove their repentance by their deeds" (NIV).
> 2. "performing deeds appropriate to repentance" (NAS).
> 3. "live lives to prove their change of heart" (NT in Modern English).

Note: Verses 9–18 contain the last of three accounts of Paul's conversion. The others are found in 9:1–19 and 22:3–21.

7 Write out **the** verse **in this chapter that** summarizes **the gospel:**

8 What **does Festus tell Paul?**

9 In essence, Festus says Paul has overdosed on the Word. Can **this happen?** ☐ Yes ☐ No Explain **your answer.**

10 Paul responded **to Festus, saying he was not mad but spoke the words of** t_____ **and** r_____.

11 What is Paul convinced of **concerning King Agrippa II?**

"None of these things escaped his attention …"
Agrippa, having lived and reigned in the Palestine area for most of his life, would have been familiar with the writings of the Old Testament prophets as well as the teachings of Christianity. Christ's ministry and resurrection would still have been well remembered by those who lived in the area.

12 With what question **did Paul put King Agrippa II on the spot?**

13 What verse suggests **that Paul's words to the king were very persuasive?**

14 What did Paul desire **for Agrippa and all those who heard him?** (See v. 29.)

15 This crisscross **puzzle contains words that describe Paul's desire for those listening to him.** Solve the puzzle by placing words from v. 29 into specific rows or columns of the puzzle.

A L T O G E T H E R

16 **What was Agrippa's conclusion about Paul's situation?** (Read vv. 31–32.)

What's It Mean?

befitting—Proper, appropriate (v. 20).

All Right!   ☐ **Yes** ☐ **No**
I read chapter 26.   ☐ **Yes, but I have questions.**

17 **Circle the word** in Acts 9:15 that indicates what **part** of Jesus' prophesy about Paul's ministry is being fulfilled in chapter 26.

But the Lord said to him, "Go, for he is a chosen vessel of Mine to bear My name before Gentiles, kings, and the children of Israel."

Key Verse

And Paul said, "I would to God that not only you, but also all who hear me today, might become both almost and altogether such as I am, except for these chains."

Acts 26:29

GO TO ROME.
GO DIRECTLY TO ROME.
DO NOT PASS "GO."
DO NOT COLLECT 200 SHEKELS.

PAUL'S JOURNEY TO ROME

| Date: A.D. 59 | Place: Caesarea to Malta | Roman Emperor: Nero | Local Ruler: Herod Agrippa II, Felix (Procurator of Judea) |

1 **With whom was Paul about to sail?**
1. Other _____ 3. A_____
2. J_____ 4. L_____

2 **Did Julius like Paul?** ☐ Yes ☐ No **Quote a verse that supports your answer.**

Do you believe this same centurion was in charge of Paul while in Caesarea?
☐ Yes ☐ No

Augustan Regiment

As a centurion, Julius would have been in charge of 100 men, or a regiment. The name of his regiment was *Augustan*, or *Imperial*. Recall that Cornelius, also a centurion, belonged to the *Italian Regiment*.

Adramyttium was a city on the coast of Mysia.

3 **Where did the centurion switch ships?**
_____

Alexandrian Ship

This would be a ship from Alexandria, Egypt, most likely carrying a cargo of grain (see v. 38).

4 **What warning did Paul give the men according to verse 10?**

After the Fast The fast mentioned here is the Day of Atonement (October 5). Because of high winds, the Romans felt that it was risky to sail after September 11, and after November 11 they did not sail at all. The ship owner must have been eager to get his cargo to Rome because they were sailing in a season known to be perilous.

5 **Why did they not stay in the harbor of Fair Havens?**
_____

Where did they want to stay for the winter?
_____

6 **Did Paul say "I told you so" in a different way?** ☐ Yes ☐ No **Explain your answer.**

Euroclydon is the Greek word meaning "northeaster," the gale-force wind that periodically blew from the northeast across the Adriatic Sea.

7 **Describe the "life assurance" policy given to Paul and the men on the ship.**

8 **This crossword is made up of words that are used when one is sailing a boat or ship. Let the clues help you find the puzzle words.**

Across

2 A measure of depth of water equaling about six feet (v. 28)
4 Weights to prevent or control the boat's movement (v. 40)
5 A small boat (v. 30)
7 Measures of the depth of water using a length of cord (v. 28)
9 The bow or front of the ship (v. 30)
10 Ropes and equipment used to help raise and lower the sails and cargo (v. 19)
11 Part of a ship that steers or turns it (v. 40)

Down

1 An area of water partially protected by land (v. 39)
3 The largest sail on a ship (v. 40)
6 To strengthen or support the underside of something (v. 17)
7 The rear of the boat (v. 29)
8 Put up the sails to catch the wind (v. 17)

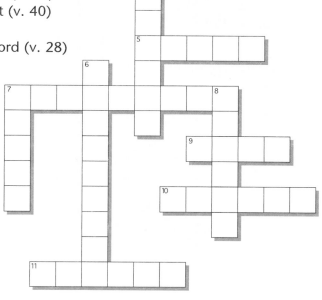

9 **How did the sailors know they were getting close to land?**

11 **How many days did they battle the storm?**

_____

12 **What did Paul urge the men to do?**

What was special about the occasion described in verse 35?

How did Paul's action affect the men's morale? (Reverse the words and letters in the phrase.)
.degaruocne erew llA

10 **Did the centurion and soldiers trust Paul's advice?** ☐ Yes ☐ No **How did they show their trust?** (Read verses 31 and 32.)

Why do you think they now believed what Paul said?

13 **How many were on the ship?**
(Circle the correct number.)

761 763 764 76 276 676 776 876 976

SOLVE THE MYSTERY

14 What did the soldiers **begin** to do before Julius stopped them?

Why did the soldiers want to **kill** all the prisoners? (Read 12:19.)

15 **Number** the following six places where Paul landed in the **order** that they are mentioned in Acts 27 and 28:1.

_____ Myra   _____ Malta

_____ Fair Havens   _____ Caesarea

_____ Sidon   _____ Cnidus

16 Write the **two methods** the men used to get to shore, and the **number** who made it safely ashore.

What **prophecies** of Paul's were **fulfilled** in verses 41–44?

 MEDITATION Christians will face trials and troubles that are, in a sense, like the literal storm Paul faced in chapter 27. He managed to live through it, and along the way he encouraged and ministered to many around him.

At the back of your workbook, write about a trial you faced, large or small. Tell how you encouraged and ministered to others as you went through it, or how others encouraged and ministered to you.

What's It Mean?

tempestuous—Uncontrollable, raging, as in a storm (v. 14).

tempest-tossed—Tossed about by a raging storm (v. 18).

 Key Verses

For there stood by me this night an angel of the God to whom I belong and whom I serve, saying "Do not be afraid, Paul; you must be brought before Caesar; and indeed God has granted you all those who sail with you."

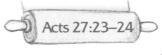 Acts 27:23–24

All Right!   ☐ Yes ☐ No
I read chapter 27. ☐ Yes, but I have questions.

Date: A.D. 59–62	Place: Malta, Rome	Roman Emperor: Nero	Local Ruler: Herod Agrippa II, Fests (Governor of Judea)

1 **On what island were Paul and his companions shipwrecked?** (Unscramble the word.)
a t M l a = _____

2 **How would you describe the people on this island?** Study verses 2 and 10.
(Circle all correct answers.)

    stingy   kind   hospitable

       generous   grumpy

3 **What did the islanders first think of Paul, and why?**

What did they say he was later, and why?

4 **Who was Publius?**

What did he do for Paul and his companions?

Dysentery
is an infection of the intestinal tract caused by a bacterium or a parasite. Its symptoms are extreme abdominal pain, bleeding, and diarrhea. Serious even today, dysentery was always life threatening prior to modern medicine.

5 **What very important act preceded Paul's healing of Publius' father?**
_____

6 **How many of the people on the island who had diseases were healed?**
(Circle one answer.)
few   some   many   all

The **Twin Brothers** on the figurehead of the ship were the Greek gods Castor and Pollux, the guardians of sailors. They were sons of Zeus, the king of the gods.

7 **How long did Paul and his companions stay at this port?**
_____

How did they leave?
_____

8 **How many days did Paul spend in each place?**
____ Syracuse   ____ Rhegium   ____ Puteoli

9 **How was Paul encouraged by his Christian brothers in verse 15?**

What was his response?

Can we encourage others just by being with them? ☐ Yes ☐ No **When might just your presence with a person be an encouragement?**

10 **Under what condition was Paul held captive in Rome?** (See vv. 16 and 30.)

11 **Whom did Paul first meet in Rome?**

What is the "hope of Israel" that verse 20 refers to? (Read Acts 24:15 and 21.)

Were the Jews curious about Christianity? ☐ Yes ☐ No **Write the verse that indicates this.**

12 **What did the Jews call "this sect" mentioned in verse 22?** (See Acts 24:5.)

_____

13 **Below, in Acts 28:23, note the word in italics, and answer the question that follows:**

So when they had appointed him a day, many came to him at his lodging, to whom he explained and solemnly *testified* of the kingdom of God, persuading them concerning Jesus from both the Law of Moses and the Prophets, from morning till evening.

What promise has now been fulfilled? (Read Acts 23:11.)

14 In verses 26 and 27 Paul is quoting Isaiah 6:9–10. **Fill in the missing words, and then summarize in one sentence what Isaiah is saying about the Jews.**

²⁶ saying, "Go to this people and say: 'Hearing you will hear, and shall _____ understand; And seeing you will see, and ___ perceive; ²⁷ For the hearts of this people have grown _____. Their ears are _____ of hearing, And their eyes they have _____, Lest they should see with their eyes and hear with their ears, Lest they should understand with their hearts and turn, So that I should heal them.' "

15 Compare **verse 28 to Acts 22:21, and write a statement** (a complete sentence) **about how these two verses are alike. Include these words:** *Jews, Gentiles, salvation, rejected,* and *preach.*

DIGGING   DEEPER

18 Paul wrote the book of Romans several years before the events in Acts 28, probably from Corinth. **Read Romans 1:8– 13. Write below the relationship between Acts 28 and the Romans passage.** Important: *The you in the Romans passage refers to the Roman believers.*

16 How long **was Paul under house arrest in Rome?** _____

17 The **PUZZLE** below is a quote fall. The letters making up the description of Paul's activity while in Rome are scrambled and arranged in columns above the blanks provided for the letters of the description. **Fill in the blank boxes, using the scrambled letters in the columns above them to find the letters for the description.**

	I	U	L		P	R	L	C	C			A	H			G	O	T	P	O	L	
P	H	T	H		B	A	E	A	E	H	E	S		A	H	E		G	O	T	P	O	L	
W	A	I	N	D	R	O	N	D	N	E	S	D		T	N	D		W	I	S	H	E	U	T

LETTERS WRITTEN FROM ROME:

During his first term in a Roman prison, Paul wrote to the churches at Ephesus, Colosse, and Philippi and to a "friend and fellow-laborer" named Philemon, who lived in Colosse. As New Testament books, these letters are called Ephesians, Colossians, Philippians, and Philemon.

Rome facts:

1. It was the capital of the Roman Empire; it is now the capital of Italy.
2. It was the home of the emperor.
3. In Paul's time the population exceeded one million.
4. Close to half the population were slaves.
5. The Romans lived with all the social problems of a greedy and pagan society.

The Rest of Paul's Story

A.D. 62   Released from first imprisonment
A.D. 62–67   Made fourth missionary journey
A.D. 63–65   Wrote 1 Timothy and Titus
A.D. 67   Second Roman imprisonment
A.D. 67–68   Wrote 2 Timothy
A.D. 68   Executed (beheaded, according
              to tradition)

What's It Mean?

figurehead—A carved image sticking out in front of a ship (v. 11).
forbidding—Not allowing, preventing (v. 31).
viper—A poisonous snake (v. 3).

MEDITATION

Reflect on your study of the book of Acts. Write five things you learned that were special to you and two things that made an impact on your life.

Things that were special to me:

1.

2.

3.

4.

5.

Things that made an impact on my life:

1.

2.

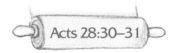

Key Verses

Then Paul dwelt two whole years in his own rented house, and received all who came to him, preaching the kingdom of God and teaching the things which concern the Lord Jesus Christ with all confidence, no one forbidding him.

Acts 28:30–31

I HAVE FOUGHT THE GOOD FIGHT, I HAVE FINISHED THE RACE, I HAVE KEPT THE FAITH.
(2 TIMOTHY 4:7)
APOSTLE PAUL A.D. 68

All Right!
I read chapter 27.
☐ Yes ☐ No
☐ Yes, but I have questions.

The Relationship Between the Jewish Groups and Offices

Council (Sanhedrin)	Scribes Teachers of the Law	Pharisees 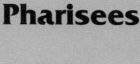
	Chief Priests High Priest	Sadducees 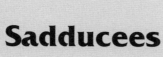
		Elders 
Priests		

Pharisees (Separatists) A group who followed the Jewish laws and traditions strictly. They prided themselves on separating from the Gentiles and were noted for their extreme legalism. This attitude has made the word *Pharisee* almost synonymous with the word *hypocrite.*

Sadducees The priestly line of Jews involved in the governing of the temple (high priests and chief priests). They were concerned with politics and the power of their position. Sadducees did not believe in any kind of resurrection, angels, or spirits. They are often referred to as the Jewish aristocrats.

scribes Also referred to as "teachers of the law" and often called "rabbis," the scribes were responsible for recording the oral traditions as well as studying and interpreting Scripture. Mainly Pharisees, the scribes were highly respected by the Jewish people.

elders Most likely leaders and/or representatives of the various Jewish tribes. They were involved in judging and counsel.

priests The great number of ordinary priests that served in the temple twice a year, for one week each time. After completing their temple duties, they would normally return home and work at other jobs.

chief priests (rulers) Permanent temple overseers in charge of worship and offerings. They were Sadducees.

high priest Leader of the temple and the only person able to enter the Holy of Holies. The high priest was head of the Sanhedrin. During Christ's trial and in the first part of Acts, Caiaphas was the high priest appointed by Herod, but Annas was the high priest recognized by the Jews. The Romans regarded the high priest as the leader of the Jews.

council (Sanhedrin) In a sense, the Jewish supreme court, made up of the chief priests, elders, and scribes. Its normal size was 71 members.

captain of the temple Captain of the temple guard (New International Version)

Essenes Though not mentioned in Acts, they were a well-known communal group of Jewish men who rejected worldly wealth. They followed strict dietary and purity laws but were not involved with those in the temple. Generally Essenes were not isolated but lived in small villages throughout the region.

Zealots The members of this antigovernment Jewish political party felt it was their religious duty to overthrow the secular rulers in control. This radically patriotic group would use any method, including murder of officials and guerrilla-like attacks on Roman gatherings. One of the apostles, James the Zealot, was once a member of this group.

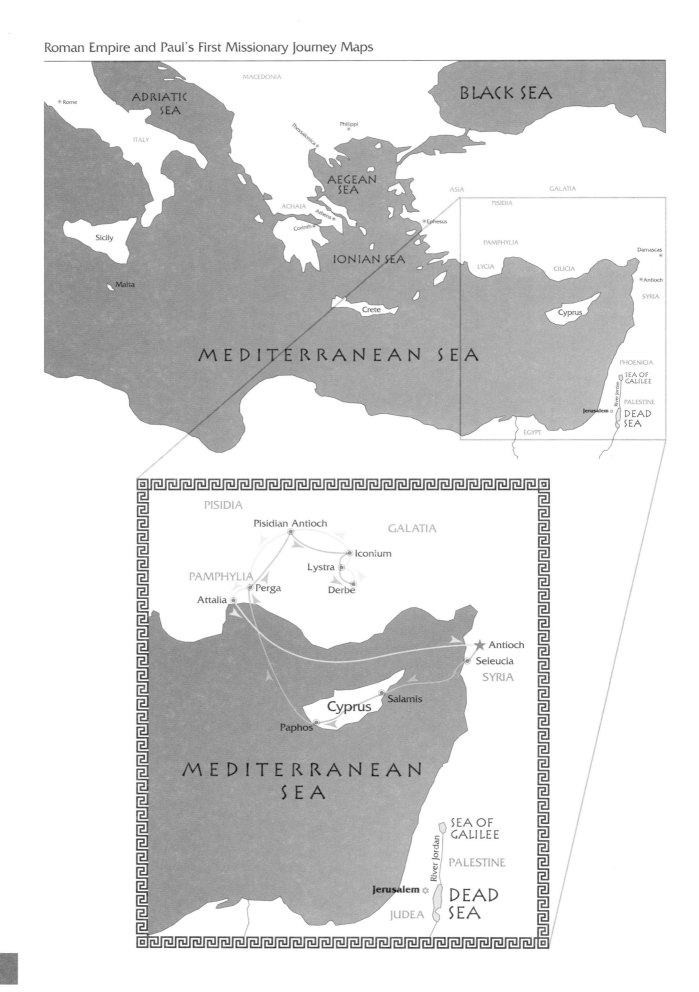

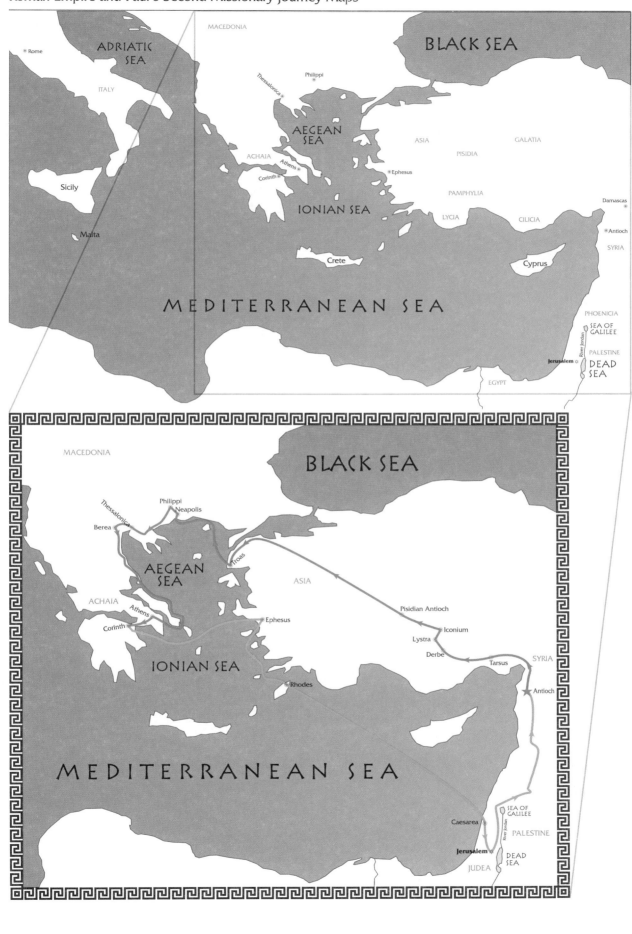

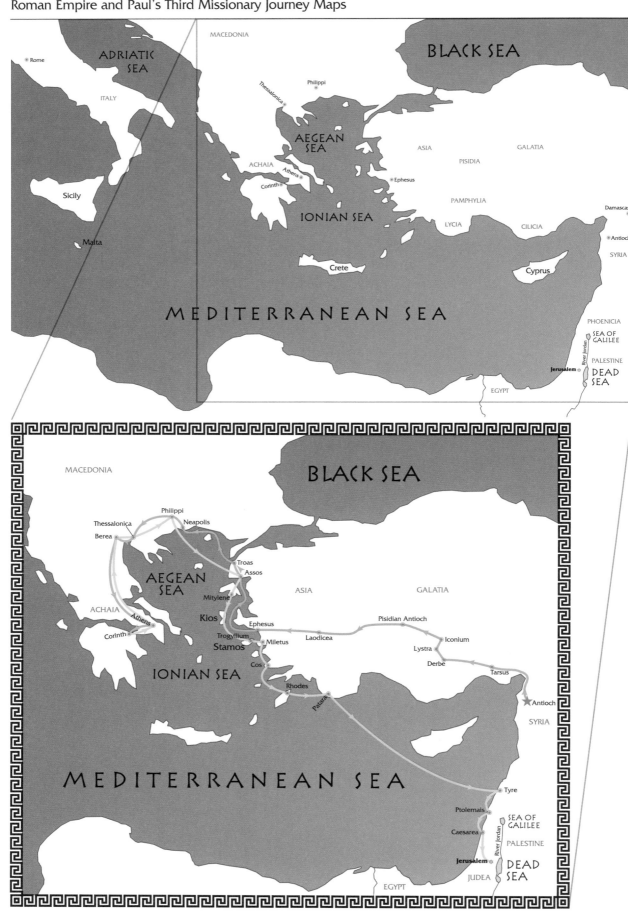

Notes, Answers, and Meditations

When writing specific answers or meditations, record the chapter and question number.

When writing specific answers or meditations, record the chapter and question number.

When writing specific answers or meditations, record the chapter and question number.

When writing specific answers or meditations, record the chapter and question number.